Magnetic Healing and

G000154781

By Larry Johnson, O.M.D., C.A.

Illustrations • Esther Platner, C. A.
Cover Illustration • Kathleen Roberts
Editing • Miriam Harris and Trish Elste
Design • Kate Degnan

Published by White Elephant Monastery
Copyright (C) 1988 By Larry Johnson   All Rights Reserved
PO Box 523
San Francisco, California 94101, USA

First Printing 1988
Printed in the United States of America
Library of Congress Catalogue Card Number 88-51529
ISBN Number 0-924071-00-1

Note to Reader and Disclaimer

The information in this book is presented for information and entertainment purposes only. All therapies, treatments, diagnoses and physical or energetic interventions of any and all natures should be undertaken only under the direct guidance and care of a properly and legally licensed, fully trained, health care professional specializing in the techniques and services rendered.

Nothing described in this book should be construed by any reader or other person to be a diagnosis or treatment for any disease or condition and neither the author or publisher can accept any responsibility for any ill effects resulting from the use or misuse of the information contained herein. Any use or misuse of the information persented here for educational and entertainment purposes is the sole responsibility of the reader. Any such use or misuse is at his or her own risk.

About the Author

Larry Johnson has been involved in energetic work for more than twenty years. His work began with training in Chinese Martial Arts and subsequently expanded to include Oriental Medicine, Chi Gung and Meditation.

In 1976, he began a yet continuing study of Wu Style Tai Chi Chuan, Taoist Chi Gung and Meditation under the private tutilage of a Taoist Master from the Hua San School.

In 1978, Larry was given the title Sifu, or Teacher, by Ming Jew, the most advanced discple of Lau Bun and present Grand Master of the Hung Sing Choy Lee Fut System of Kung Fu.

After completing a seven month acupuncture study program at Chakpori-Ling in 1977, Larry continued his study of Oriental Medicine with Peter Lam until 1978. Larry graduated from the North American College of Acupuncture in August, 1980 and from the California Acupuncture College in 1982. Also in 1982, Larry passed the California State Examination for Licensed Acupuncturist. He has practiced Acupuncture professionally in California since that time.

On the 15th of December, 1983, Larry received his Doctor of Oriental Medicine (O. M. D.) degree from the California Acupuncture College.

During succeeding years, Larry has continued to attend seminars and to study with the goal of expanding his knowledge of Oriental Medicine and finding new applications of this knowledge to benefit a larger segment of the population, especially those involved in one of the energetic development paths.

Dedication

This book is dedicated to all sincere practitioners of the Oriental Healing Arts whose efforts in the clinic, classroom, study hall and training ground enrich us all.

Acknowledgements

I would like to thank Tae-Woo Yoo, author of *Koryo Hand Acupuncture*, for his superhuman effort in bringing that system to light. I would also like to thank by name Yoshio Manaka, Kiiko Matsumoto, Steven Birch, Miki Shima, Jay Sordean and Masu Iriye for their work in rediscovering the old in the new and sharing those discoveries with the Oriental Medical Community through seminars and publications.

My heart goes out in thanks to the countless others throughout the ages who have kept this knowledge alive and opened themselves to the infinite chi so that the knowledge might flourish.

Finally, I would like to thank my taoist sifu, who wishes to remain unnamed, for providing the tools and inspiration for my path and Esther Platner for her selfless support for this work and for sharing my path.

Table of Contents

Introduction

This book is a compilation of the work of many others and my personal experience in clinically transposing their ideas onto the Koryo Hand Acupuncture model of human body energetics.

The basic theories expounded here are not new and have been clinically tested for many years using the traditional body acupuncture model. What is new, I believe, is the transposition of these techniques to the magnet modality of treatment and the energetic system of Koryo Hand Acupuncture and their use for both healing and energetic development.

This book is basically geared for the practicing acupuncturist, although a large cross section of the Wholistic Community may indeed find it useful. It does presuppose a basic knowledge of Traditional Oriental Medical Theory; yet the information presented is clear enough to be utilized by many other disciplines. The diagnostic and therapeutic techniques are presented in such a way as to be useable in the clinic *now*!

To keep with the practical spirit of the book, I will omit historical background and try to confine the lists and tables of information to an absolute minimum necessary for clinical implementation of the material presented.

I do suggest that the reader digest the material presented by Tae-Woo Yoo in his book, *Koryo Hand Acupuncture*. Although the basic, need to know information is presented here. Doctor Yoo's book would give a much deeper and broader view of hand acupuncture and its many levels of therapy.

This book is a beginning, a seed to be sown in the collective mind of the Wholistic Community. With the water of our imagination and the sunshine of hard work, I believe this seed can grow and eventually bear a mature fruit that will be a great benefit to all of mankind.

Basic Concepts of Oriental Medicine

Oriental Medicine is a vast subject that could fill a library and still not be exhausted. This chapter will present a very brief outline of the basic concepts of Oriental Medicine that will be helpful for understanding the information presented in later chapters.

Oriental Medical theory postulates that the origin of all things is the Tao, which is beyond all comprehension and understanding by the intellect. From the Tao come the Yin/Yang theory of opposites and from the Yin and Yang develop the Five Elements. Everything in existence may be classified as being associated with the Yin or Yang aspect of one or more of the Five Elements.

Oriental Medicine views all existence as a vast arena of interconnected relationships any part of which cannot be separated energetically from any other part. This is truly a wholistic view of the universe.

Yin and Yang

Yin and Yang are the two opposing, yet interdependent and complementary, aspects of all existence. They can be used to describe the relationships between and qualities of all things. Imbalances in any one or more of the Yin/Yang aspects of our being denotes illness. The function of the Oriental Medicine Practitioner is to locate these imbalances and correct them, either through traditional methods such as massage, herbs, acupuncture and exercises or through more modern approaches like electro-acupuncture, ion pumping and magnets.

The basic properties of Yang simulate those of fire and the basic properties of Yin simulate those of water.

Yang is hot, bright, rising, expanding, daytime, spring, summer, external, etc. Yin is cold, dim, sinking, contracting, nighttime, fall, winter, internal, etc. Yang relates to the bowels of the human body and Yin relates to the viscera of the human body.

The bowels are considered external and the viscera considered internal in their relationship to each other.

Because Yin and Yang are so closely connected and interdependent, any imbalance in one of them will soon affect the other. They are involved in a constantly changing energetic play called life. The play is staged within certain limits called balance. When these limits are breached by either Yin or Yang, there is sickness. Death, signifying the total divorce of the Yin/Yang relationship, is the end of the play.

Five Elements

From Yin and Yang develop the Five Elements — water, wood, fire, earth and metal. These terms do not denote the actual physical manifestations of water, wood, fire, earth and metal but point towards an energetic quality represented by them. The ancients observed the cycles of birth, growth, maturity, harvest and storage. To these they applied the element names. The various interactions between the elements can be used to chart the course of a mans life or the progression of a disease. Diagnosis and treatment of disease as well as a profound understanding of the natural cycles of life can be realized through a serious study of the Five Elements.

The Five Elements are involved in the constantly changing energetic play of life in regular observable cycles. Every aspect of the universe can be associated with either the Yin or Yang polarity of one of the elements.

The promoting or growth cycle is easy to grasp. The elements are arranged in a pentagon with each corner of the pentagon representing one of the elements. As we go around the pentagon, each element is the mother of the one it precedes and the son of the one it follows. The mother nourishes the son, and the son receives from the mother. The order is as follows: Water (mother) nourishes Wood (son) - Wood (mother) nourishes Fire (son) - Fire (mother) nourishes Earth (son) - Earth (mother) nourishes Metal (son) and Metal (mother) nourishes Water (son).

Five Element Correspondences

	Wood	Fire	Earth	Metal	Water
Viscera	liver	heart pericardium	spleen	lung	kidney
Bowel	gall bladder	sm. intest. triple burner	stomach	large intestine	urinary bladder
Color	green	red	yellow	white	black blue
Emotion	anger	joy	remini- scence	grief sorrow	fear fright
Tissue	tendon	blood vessel	muscle	skin	bone
Sense Organ	eyes	tongue	mouth	nose	ears
Season	spring	summer	late summer	fall	winter
Taste	sour	bitter	sweet	pungent	salty
Direction	east	south	middle	west	north
Climate	wind	heat	damp	dry	cold
Nature	birth	growth	mature	harvest	store
Sound	shout	laugh	sing	weep	groan
Liquid Emitted	tears	sweat	saliva	mucous	urine
Grain	wheat	millet	rye	rice	beans
Meat	chicken	mutton	beef	horse	pork
Nourishes	nails	complexion	lips	body hair	head hair

To balance this growth cycle, we have the control cycle. In this philosophical concept, each element has an element that controls or restrains it. This holds unbalanced growth in check. The control cycle follows this order: Water controls Fire, Fire controls Metal, Metal controls Wood, Wood controls Earth, and Earth controls Water.

When these cycles are working smoothly and in harmony, we have balance. If we have an excess or deficiency in any one of the elements, there will soon be other imbalances created through the interrelated cycles. For example, if Wood becomes weakened, it may draw too much from its mother, Water, and will not feed its son, Fire, enough. It may not be able to properly control Earth and can become overcontrolled by Metal. Furthermore, the imbalances resulting in the other elements due to the weakness in wood can create other problems in their cyclic relationships. It is within this theoretical framework that diagnosis by Five Elements takes place and the proper balancing therapy is planned.

Five Element Cycles

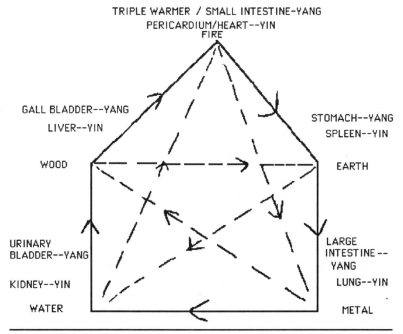

The Twelve Major Organs and Meridians

There are six major Yin organs and six major Yang organs (counting the Pericardium-Yin and the triple burner-Yang, which are functions rather than physical organs). The organs are grouped in internally/externally related pairs of one Yin and one Yang organ.

Each organ has an associated energetic pathway or meridian connecting it to the periphery and to other organs in the whole body's energetic system. The meridians circulate vital energy and blood, warm and nourish the tissues, and link and support the various structural and functional aspects of the whole being. The meridians also provide the route for internal man to communicate with the cosmos.

If one area of the body is in a state of imbalance, the pathology may spread via the meridian system to other areas of the body. Likewise, areas of imbalance may be treated via the meridian system.

Yang Organs

The main functions of the Yang Organs are to receive and digest food, to absorb nutrients and to, excrete waste material.

The Gall Bladder forms a Yin/Yang pair with the Liver. Its main functions are to store bile and secrete it into the Small Intestine to aid digestion. It is the only Yang organ that stores a pure liquid (bile).

The Stomach forms a Yin/Yang pair with the Spleen. Its main functions are to receive and decompose food, temporarily store it, and pass it to the Small Intestine for further digestion.

The Small Intestine forms a Yin/Yang pair with the Heart. Its main functions are to receive partially digested food from the Stomach, temporarily store it and assimilate nutrients, and pass on the residue to the Large Intestine for excretion.

The Lower Burner is the hypogastric area and general-izesthe functions of the Urinary Bladder and Kidneys in controlling water metabolism. It is also the residence of our pre-natal, or source, vital energy which is our inherited constitutional energy.

Yin Organs

The main functions of the Yin organs are to manufacture and store essential substances such as vital essence, vital energy, and body fluids.

The Heart is Yin/Yang paired with the Small Intestine and is considered the overall ruler of the body, home of Shen.(the controlling spirit of the body), its main functions are to control the blood and vessels and to house the mind.

The Liver is Yin/Yang paired with the Gall Bladder. Its main functions are to store blood, nourish the tendons, and maintain the smooth flow of vital energy throughout the whole body, especially in the Spleen and Stomach.

The Spleen (including the Pancreas) is Yin/Yang related to the Stomach. Its main functions are to govern digestion, absorption and transmission of nutrients to the body, keep the blood in the vessels, hold the internal organs in place, and nourish the muscles. It is also deeply involved in water metabolism.

The Lungs are Yin/Yang related to the Large Intestine. The main functions of the Lungs are to control respiration, regulate the water passages and nourish the skin and hair. Regulating the water passages refers to the functions of turning part of the body fluid into sweat to be excreted through the pores in the skin, controlling the pores and energetically sending part of the body fluid down to the Kidney/Urinary Bladder complex.

The Kidney is Yin/Yang paired with the Urinary Bladder. Its main functions are to store essential substances, dominate reproduction, growth, and development, produce marrow, control the bones and body fluids, manufacture blood through the marrow, and receive and control air from the Lungs.

The Large Intestine is Yin/Yang paired with Lung. Its main function is to receive from the Small Intestine, absorb part of the liquid, and turn the rest to feces, and transport the feces to the anus for excretion.

The Urinary Bladder is Yin/Yang paired with the Kidneys. Its main functions are to temporarily store urine and discharge it when the proper amount is in storage.

The Triple Burner is Yin/Yang paired with the Pericardium. Both are functions rather than physical organs. Although the Triple Burner is classified as a Yang organ, it is really the combination of the physiological activities of three areas of the body:

> The Upper Burner is the chest area and generalizes the functions of the Lung and Heart in transporting blood andvital energy throughout the body.

> The Middle Burner is the epigastric area and general-izesthe functions of the Spleen and Stomach in digesting food and absorbing nutrients.

The Pericardium is Yin/Yang related to the Triple Burner. Its main functions are to protect the Heart and relay orders from the Heart to the rest of the body.

Life Energy

A fertilized egg is the combination of life essence from the father and the mother and the infusion of Heavenly Spirit. This combination produces the basic constitutional energy upon which the physical and mental potential of the individual depends — the Source Chi. In the womb, the Source Chi is nourished by the mother. After birth its nourishment comes from the work of the organs.

The body calls upon energy from the Source Chi to aid in digestion, combat illness, and handle any emergency that requires extra life energy. The strength of the Source Chi determines the length of one's life. There is much controversy over whether

Source Chi may be replaced if dissipated. Some authorities maintain that it can only be dissipated while others believe that through various means including Chi Kung (Breathing Exercises), Martial Arts and certain Oriental Medical Techniques, the Source Chi can be slowly replaced.

The body transforms food and air into life energy as follows. The food is eaten and passes to the Stomach. Here energy from the Source Chi drives off the energetic essence from the food and the Spleen directs this essence to the Lungs. In the Lungs the essence of food is mixed with the essence of the air we breathe and this mixture is acted upon by energy from the Source Chi to form Life Energy that circulates in the Meridians. This Life Energy divides into two functionally different forms, one for nourishing the body and one for protecting the body from external pathogens.

The various systems of the body use the life energy according to their needs. If there is a surplus, it is stored in the Kidneys where it can be called upon in time of need. The Kidneys use some of the stored energy to produce reproductive energy.

If the digestive system is working well, sufficient energy will be produced to meet the body's needs. If the digestive system is not working well or disease, deprivation or trauma, rob the body of energy, stored energy from the Kidneys will be used. If there is not enough energy stored in the Kidneys to meet the body's needs, Source Chi will be depleted and life shortened. Excess sexual activity will have the same effect— draining Kidney energy and shortening life.

Energy is not the only product of digested food. The grosser elements of the food(vitamins, minerals, physical nutrients, etc.) are absorbed by the gastrointestinal system to be turned into blood and other body fluids which are used to nourish and maintain the physical body. Many people believe that life energy (Vital Force) can be increased by various methods such as meditation, martial arts, or Yoga.

The basic idea here is that increasing the flow of vital force through various energy centers in the body causes the body to function more efficiently and thereby increases the production of vital energy. Some people even believe that it is possible to absorb and transform energy directly from the universe.

If we look at Chi (Energy) as the basic building block of creation and all else as but a different manifestation of this Chi, we can see the possibilities.

Pathology

In Oriental Medicine disease is caused by three classes of pathogenic factors: external, internal and miscellaneous. If any of these factors is stronger than the resistance of the body, disease will result.

External pathogenic factors include wind, cold, summer heat, damp, dryness and Fire. The vital activities of the body are closely related to weather conditions. Our normal adaptive ability allows us to perform well under normal weather conditions but if we are in a state of depletion or severe weather conditions occur, pathogenic factors may invade our body and cause disease.

Internal pathogenic factors are excess or deficiency of one or more in the seven emotions: Joy, Grief, Anger, Reminiscence, Worry, Fear, or Fright. Normally, we experience a full range of these emotions in our daily life but if one or more become unbalanced both psychological and physiological problems can occur.

Miscellaneous causes of disease cover a wide range of factors including diet, stress, overwork, lack of exercise, trauma, poison, animal or insect bourne diseases and morality or social custom problems.

Traditional Diagnosis

Traditional Diagnosis is accomplished through four basic methods:
• The first is *observation* of the patient's expression, posture, color, skin condition, tongue, etc.

- The second is *recognition* of sounds and odors that emanate from the patient.
- The third method is to *question* the patient.
- The fourth method is to *palpate* various areas on the patient's body to experience physical or energetic abnormalities. Some of the common areas to palpate are meridian pathways, pulses, specific alarm points, and the abdomen.

The Eight Extraordinary Vessels

The eight Extraordinary Vessels are energetic pathways that are not related to particular organs. They function as reservoirs to store and regulate energy and intermingle with the twelve major meridians.

Du Mo: The Governing Vessel—Sea of Yang—governs all the Yang channels of the body

Ren Mo: The Conception Vessel—Sea of Yin—governs all the Yin channels of the body

Chong Mo: Vitality/Strategic—Sea of Meridians—communicates with all the channels of the body

Dai Mo: Girdle—binds all the channels at the waist like a belt

Yang Chaio Mo: Heel—controls all movement of Yang in the body

Yin Chaio Mo: Heel—controls all the movement of Yin in the body

Yang Wei Mo: Links—connect all the Yang channels in the body

Yin Wei Mo: Links—connect all the Yin channels in the body

These eight Extraordinary Vessels are very useful in the clinic for pain and structural problems. They are alsoimportant channels of development in Taoist Yoga.

Divergent Meridians

The Divergent Meridians are branches of the twelve major meridians that bring Yin to the head, link the Yin and Yang paired organs at a deep level, bring vital energy to areas not reached by the major meridians and bring protective energy to the organs. Therapy at this deep level is useful for chronic and very old imbalances.

Lo or Connecting Channels

The Lo channels are also branches of the twelve major meridians and serve to connect the major meridians to their Yin/Yang paired meridian. The Ren and Du channels also have Los and the Spleen has its regular Lo plus a Great Lo which is said to control the blood of the whole body. This makes a total of fifteen Lo Channels.

Magnets

Sticking to the practical, I will not go into the history of healing with magnets nor an in depth study of magnetic field theory. Rather,I will present the basic material needed for understanding the diagnostic and therapeutic techniques discussed later in the text.

Oriental Medicine, at heart, is based upon Yin/Yang theory — the mutual support/contention of the ultimate opposites. Diagnosis is aimed at discovering the relative imbalances of these opposites in our energetic system and therapy seeks to restore that balance between them.

Magnets the epitomize of the energetic manifestation of the Yin/Yang theory. Magnets can be produced to define clearly the opposites (north pole/south pole), and thus provide (through their magnetic field) a very precise therapeutic and diagnostic tool.

Evidence shows that magnetic fields do affect the vital energy of the human body in predictable ways and, of course, affecting the vital energy of the body is the basic principal of therapy in Oriental Medicine. Through the use of magnets, a precise and predictable method of diagnosis and therapy may be achieved.

In his book *Koryo Hand Acupuncture*, Doctor Tae-Woo Yoo suggests that magnets exert influence through their effect on hemoglobin in the blood. Hemoglobin does contain a large amount of iron. This is one very possible explanation. In addition, I also believe that the magnetic field itself will affect our own bio-chemical electro-magnetic energy, our life force.

Magnets of different strengths produce different effects on our energetic system when used with both traditional body acupuncture points and Koryo Hand Acupuncture points. There are several varieties of magnets available on the market today. I have been using magnets in clinic for several years and find that the 600 Gause magnets designed for Hand Acupuncture give the best results for all of the techniques covered in this book. These techniques give the best results of any method I have ever used in diagnosis and therapy.

As stated before, magnets epitomize the energetic manifestation of Yin and Yang. They constitute a comfortable "given" in the complex and subtle world of energetic medicine.

Magnetic field energy flows from north to south (N——>S). In so doing, this energy field influences other energy fields it comes into contact with—for our purposes, the meridians and acupoints of hand acupuncture. In practice, this means that a pair of opposite poles attached to a meridian at specific spots can be utilized either to tonify (add energy to) or to sedate (disperse energy from) that meridian, depending on the arrangement of the poles. It also means that as energy is drawn to a south pole it has a tonifying effect, and as energy is drawn from a north pole it has a sedating effect, as long as the magnets are within the same influential energetic system. These basic principals are used in diagnosis and treatment, as we shall see.

Magnet therapy has the advantage of being physically non-invasive. In this time of public concern for sterile technique, that is a big plus. Although magnet therapy is non-invasive, many patients report the feeling of needle sensation at the site of the magnet and also propagated sensation. This does not appear to have a direct relationship to the effectiveness of treatment.

Magnets can also be taped to the patient's hand and worn for several days. This is very useful in pain conditions and in general therapy. In many cases, the patient can learn to apply the magnets himself. This is necessary in the augmentation of meditation, martial arts and athletic performance.

It is very important to explain the signs of shock (needle sickness) to any patients intending to wear or apply the magnets outside the clinic.. Great care must be taken to ensure the proper north south pole alignment in application. Too much stimulation over a period of time can also produce needle sickness.

If the patient is in the clinic, any of the usual acupuncture techniques for shock therapy may be employed. If out of the clinic, the patient should be told to take the magnets off, drink a warm beverage, and lie down to rest. It is also important to let the patient know that if one magnet comes off the other one should be removed as well. They work in conjunction with each other and the balance will be destroyed if one is missing. This could lead to problems.

Except in certain local treatments where a north magnet may be applied alone, I always apply one north for every south in place. The energetics of magnet therapy is different than simply tonifying and sedating individual points and it is important to maintain balance in the system.

Always muscle test your patient after the treatment has been applied to be sure that the therapy is strengthening the whole energy system (more on muscle testing in the next chapter).

There is no even needling technique with magnets. In cases where even needling is called for, I use an ear tack to needle the hand acupuncture point. These tacks may also be left in place for several days. We will go into this subject more in the chapter on local treatment.

Precautions with magnet therapy are the same for regular acupuncture. Patients should not be treated if they are drunk, overtired from work, intoxicated, emotionally overstimulated, over hungry, dehydrated, extremely weak or anxious. Pregnant women should not be treated on any point corresponding to a location on the lower back, on the abdomen below the navel, or on any point corresponding to the location of a major nerve such as LI4 or SP6.

Magnets may be obtained through Common Sense Alternatives, PO Box 850, Brookline, MA 02147 or The Koryo Hand Acupuncture Institute of America, Inc., 100 Ellsworth Avenue, Suite 611, San Mateo, CA 94401, 415•348•4292.

When magnets arrive from either company listed above they come on pre-cut adhesive plasters. The south side of the magnet is attached to the plaster so the side you see is the north side. Occasionally, magnets are reversed, so it is wise to test each magnet before use. Also, since the magnets are reusable but the plasters aren't, it is necessary to know how to find the north and south sides on any magnet.

To find the north or south side of any magnet it is necessary to have a test magnet available with known polarities marked. The easy way to do this is to buy a batch of 800 gause magnets, the type with the north side marked with a small raised dot. Once you have a known polarity it is easy to find the unknown. North is attracted to south and vice-versa. With a known polarity, simply let the unknown magnet stick to the known to determine the polarity of the unknown. The north side of one will always stick to the south side of the other.

The following quote, from page 144 of *Extraordinary Vessels*, by Kiiko Matsumoto and Steven Birch, relates to the use of combined metal and magnet therapy on body acupuncture points.

> "When treating extraordinary vessels, the master point receives copper, gold, or the north magnet; the coupled point receives the zinc, aluminum, or the south magnetic pole. On the twelve meridians, when treating a painfull or sensitive area (an excess condition), zinc, aluminum or the north magnetic pole are used. A distal point, or a deficient meridian, takes the copper, gold or south facing magnet. Thus, the polarity reverses when not using the extraordinary vessels."

The information pertinent to our study is that north magnetic or south magnetic fields affect the twelve body meridians in a different way than do the eight extraordinary vessels. In other words, if gold or copper are used on one of the twelve body meridians to tonify a point, a south magnet is appropriate; and if gold or copper are used on the master point of one of the extraordinary meridians, a north magnet is appropriate. By the same token, a zinc or aluminum needle and north magnetic field will sedate points on the twelve body meridians, and for the coupled point of an extraordinary meridian treatment a zinc or aluminum needle, or a south magnetic field, is used.

Clinical experience with hand acupuncture shows a different energetic effect with magnets. Here, if one uses combined metal therapy and magnets we find that a gold or copper needle (or a south magnetic field) will still tonify a point on the twelve hand meridians which tonify the same point on the body meridians. And a zinc or aluminum needle (or a north magnetic field) will sedate a point on the hand meridians which will sedate the same point on the body meridians. However, if a gold or copper needle is used to treat the master point of an extraordinary meridian, a south magnetic field is used; and if a zinc or aluminum needle is used to treat the coupled point, a north magnetic field is used.

I believe the answer to this apparent contradiction lies in the difference in the method of actual stimulation to the actual extraordinary vessels and twelve meridians. In the case of body points, the needle or magnetic field is itself directly stimulating the pertinent energy system. In the case of hand acupuncture, I believe the hand micromeridian corresponding to the pertinent system in the body—not the needle or magnetic field applied to the hand microsystem—is stimulating the extraordinary vessel or regular meridian. In other words, the hand meridians mediate the therapeutic stimulation and energetically affect the systems in the body. It is the state or quality of energy in the hand that affects the systems in the body, not the cause of that state. Both the hand microsystems and the twelve body meridians are external in relation to the Eight Extraordinary Vessels, so magnetic energy affects them in the same way. The Eight Extraordinary Vessel are more internal and, when acted upon directly with magnets, respond opposite the external systems.

Tools

There are two important tools used in the diagnosis techniques covered in this book. Both are easily made as explained below.

The first tool, called a bar magnet, is a simple arrangement of six magnets glued to a small piece of wood (see illustration). The idea is to have three magnets with the north side facing outwards on one end of the wood and three magnets with the south side facing outward on the other end. This creates a magnetic field flow from the north end to the south end. The piece of wood should be about 1¼ in length and just wide enough to accommodate the magnets. The magnets themselves should be evenly spaced with a slightly larger space between the innermost north and south poles. This spacing will be important later for our diagnostic technique.

BAR MAGNETS

Bottom

North   South

Top

North   South

The second tool, called a cylinder magnet, is made by inserting a round magnet (a regular 800 gause magnet is used, not the hand acupuncture magnets used with the previous tool) into a 1 inch section of plastic straw. The magnet is set so that the north side faces one of the openings of the straw and the south side faces the other opening of the straw. Take two Q-Tips, dip each in glue and insert one Q-Tip in each end of the straw. Be sure to mark the end of the straw with the north side pointing towards its opening. When the glue dries, clip the Q-Tip handles to convenient length, which will be just slightly longer that the straw. The purpose of these tools will be explained in detail later.

Cylinder Magnet

1
Cut a 1 inch section from
a plastic straw.

2
Insert a round 800 gause
magnet into the center of
the straw.

3

Take two Q-tips, dip each in glue and insert
one Q-tip into each end of the straw with the
North side darkened.After the glue has dried

4
After the glue has dried, clip the Q-tip handles
to a length slightly longer than the straw.

System Testing

In Oriental Medicine, the human body is looked upon as a whole energy system. In theory, weakening any part of the system will weaken the whole system. and strengthening any part of the system will strengthen the whole system.

For the purposes of diagnosis and treatment with magnets, it is necessary to have a method whereby we can ascertain if a treatment is diagnostic technique or strengthening the whole system or weakening the whole system. We use muscle testing or testing the kinethesiologic response of this purpose. The basic principal is that if a certain arrangement of magnets is strengthening to the system, the muscle test response will become stronger and if the arrangement is weakening to the system, the muscle test response will become weaker.

There are many ways of choosing the points to be used and of arranging the polarity of the magnets. A method of checking on the overall system's energetic response to each step of the diagnosis and treatment is necessary to ensure proper therapy. In the clinic, I most often use a simple version of the O-ring test. This test, developed by Doctor Omura, is easy to use, and for most patients is quite clearly shows the relative strengthening or weakening of the overall energy system.

To perform the O-ring test, ask the patient to hold one of their fingers tip to tip with their thumb on the same hand (see illustration). Then ask the patient to resist while you pull the finger and thumb gently, but firmly, apart. You can use any finger as long as the result is clear. For strong patients, you will have to use a weaker finger. For most patients, the thumb and index finger work nicely.

O-Ring Test

If you subject the body to a beneficial influence, the finger-grip should become stronger and a harmful influence will cause the grip to weaken. This technique can also be used to choose herbal formulas, acupoints and all means of diagnostic and therapeutic methods. For herbal remedies, simply have the patient hold the formula in one hand and test the other. If the test makes them stronger, the formula is good for them, and if weaker, it is the wrong formula.

Another simple technique that works well is to have your patient hold their arm outstretched at shoulder level. Have the patient resist while you push down on the arm. Perform the same test while employing your diagnostic or therapeutic intervention to see if the technique weakens or strengthens their energetic system.

With experience, many practitioners can feel the energetic change by merely touching the patient. Also, a surprising number of patients report being able to sense the change themselves before the practitioner touches them.

If the patient is too weak to do the test himself, or some other circumstance prevents his participation, anther person can hold the patient's hand with one of their hands and you can test the second person's other hand. By joining hands, the two people become one energetic system in a sense and that phenomenon can be used for testing.

During testing, the practitioner should keep a clear mind and ask the patient to be calm. The practitioner can then mentally ask for the needed information—"is this good for the patient?" etc.

I am sure that there are other tests which are just as effective that may be employed for the same purposes. The important thing is that we have some feedback from the system itself to show how we are affecting it.

Hand Acupuncture

Hand acupuncture, as developed by Doctor Yoo, is a system of therapy based upon using the meridian systems of the hand. Doctor Yoo discovered that the hand contains a micro-system comparable to the traditional energy system of the body. The hand micro-system directly influences the body in approximately the same way as the more traditional body system. All of the laws of Traditional Oriental Medical Theory apply to hand acupuncture in the same way as body acupuncture, and many of the treatment plans applied to the body can be applied to the hand with at least equivalent therapeutic results.

It is not in the scope of this work to do an in depth study of Doctor Yoos' system. I will present the basic meridian system and the points necessary to utilize the therapies discussed in later chapters. The following illustrations show the meridian pathways, the direction of energy flow, and the point locations for Doctor Yoos' point numbering system with the corresponding traditional points labeled where available. The body correspondence charts will follow in the chapter on local treatment. Traditional body meridian charts are also presented to equate flow patterns on hand and body.

In this system, you will see that each hand has a complete representation of the traditional energy system of the body. (This will be utilized in the treatment plans presented later.) Generally speaking, if a problem manifests on the right side of the body, the right hand is used for therapy, and if the problem is on the left side, the left hand is used. The two ulnar fingers are usually used for treatment, unless the problem is very stubborn, in which case the radial fingers of the opposite side hand can be used.

In several of the therapies presented later in this book we needed to use points that Dr. Yoo did not provide correspondences for in his text. We found these point locations by stressing the traditional body points with a magnet until the system was weakened (by muscle test response) and applying the opposite pole magnet to hand points until we found the one that counteracted the stress to the body points. Clinical experience has shown us that these point locations are valid and have the desired effect.

Energy in the meridians flows from the smaller number towards the larger number: 1————> 8, 9, 10, etc. In the following diagrams, I have included both the Korean hand point numbering system, left side, and the traditional body points, right side, to which they correspond.

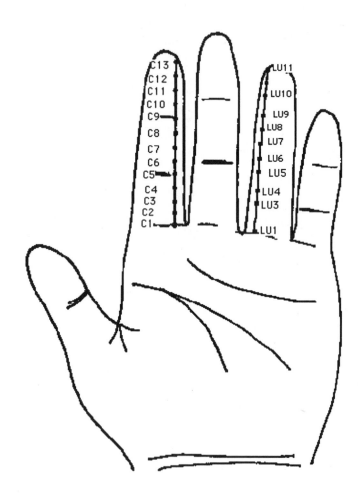

Lung Channel - body

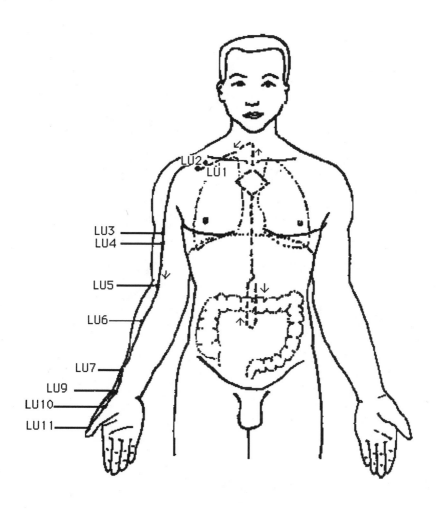

Large Intestine Channel- hand

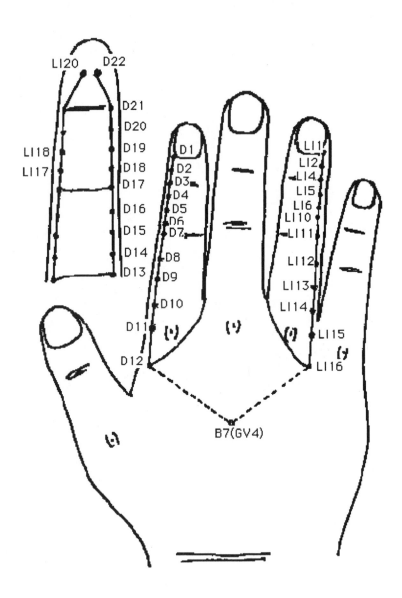

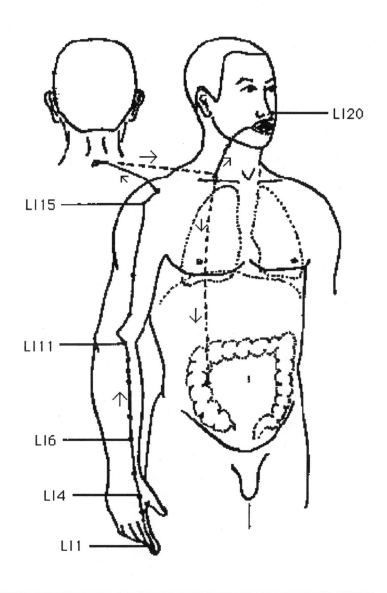

LI20

LI15

LI11

LI6

LI4

LI1

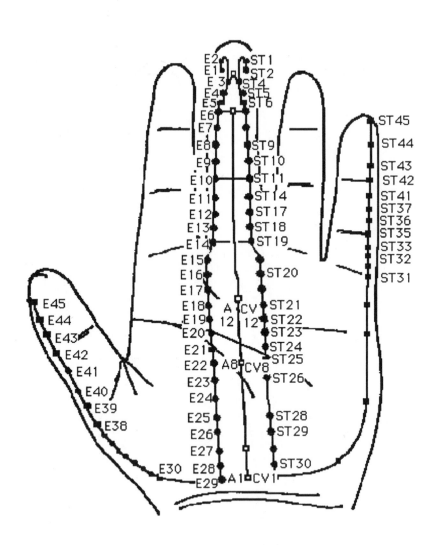

Stomach Channel - body

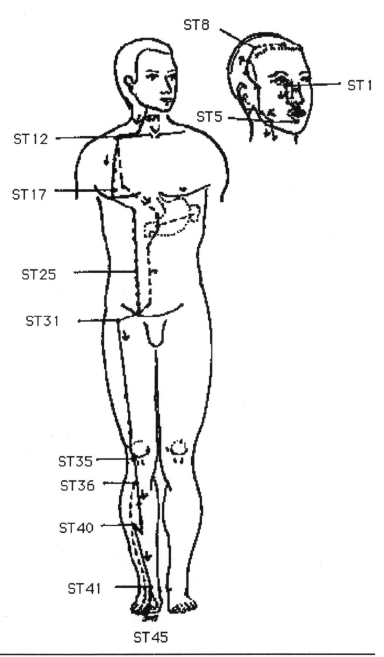

Spleen Channel - hand

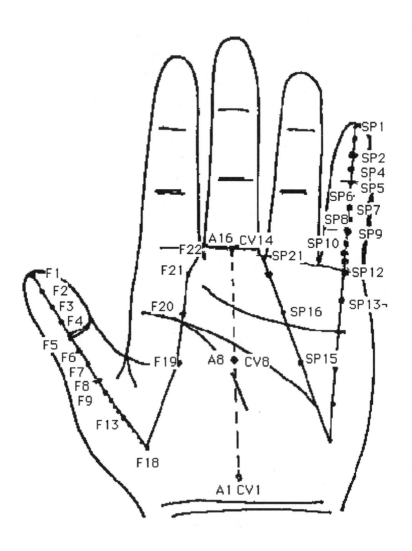

Spleen Channel - body

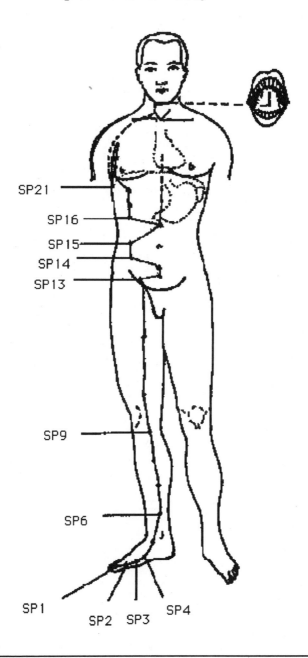

SP21
SP16
SP15
SP14
SP13

SP9

SP6

SP1

SP2   SP3   SP4

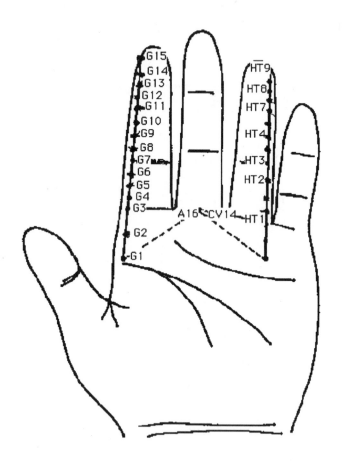

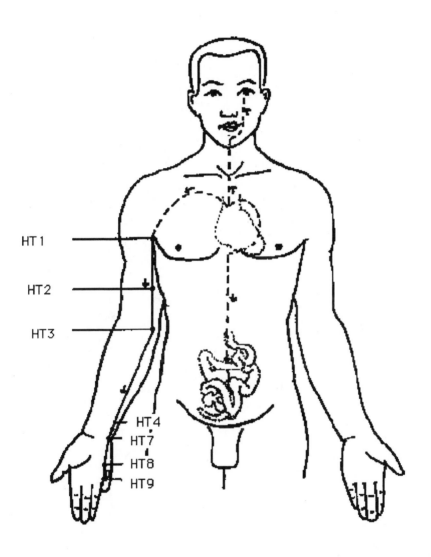

HT 1

HT 2

HT 3

HT 4
HT 7
HT 8
HT 9

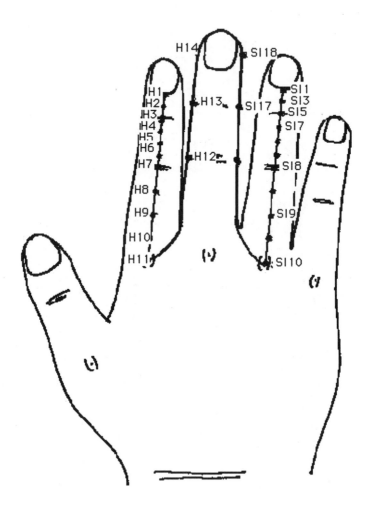

Small Intestine - body

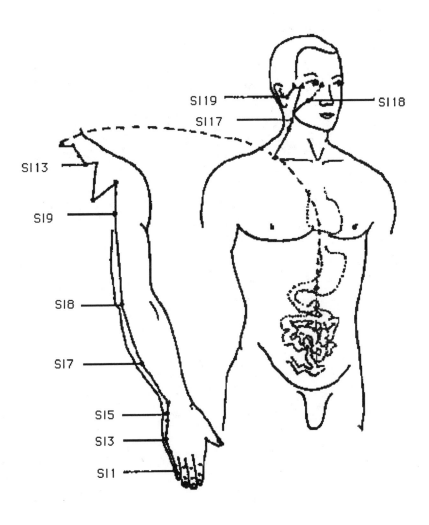

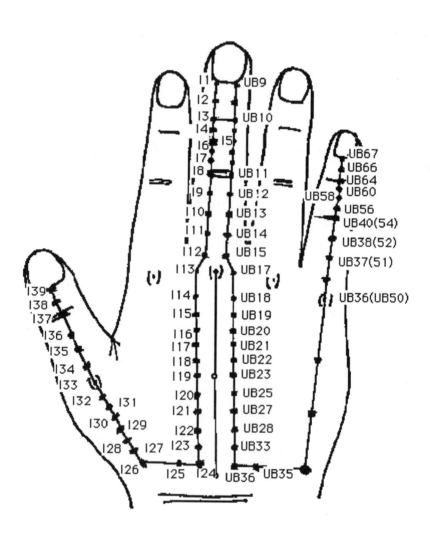

Urinary Bladder Channel - body

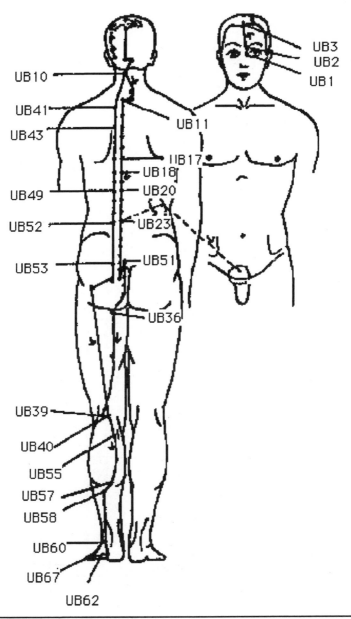

UB10
UB41
UB43
UB49
UB52
UB53

UB11
IIB17
UB18
UB20
UB23
UB51
UB36

UB3
UB2
UB1

UB39
UB40
UB55
UB57
UB58
UB60
UB67
UB62

Kidney Channel - hand

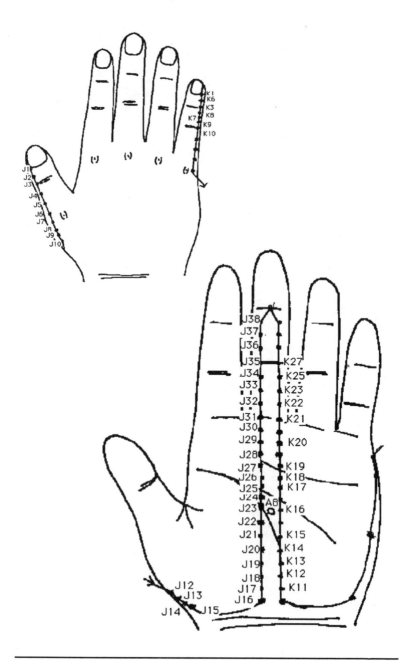

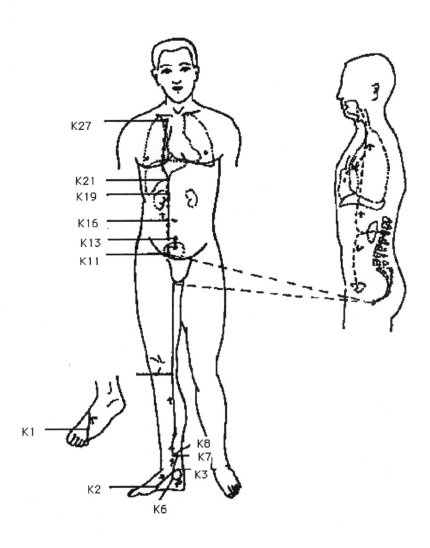

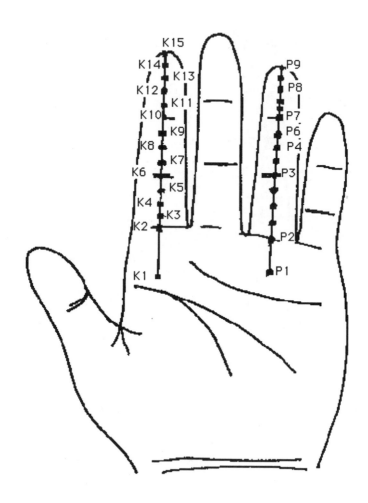

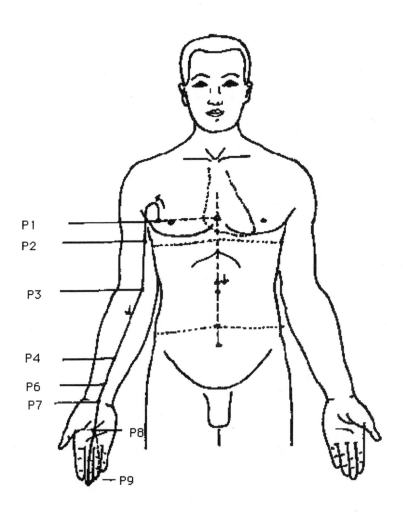

Triple Burner Channel - hand

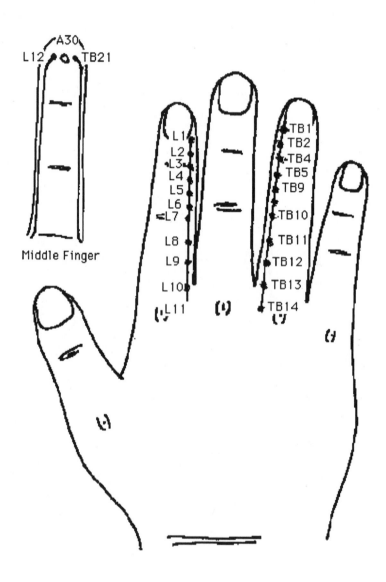

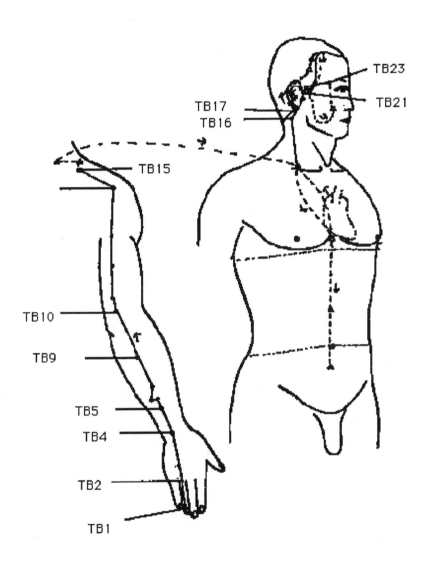

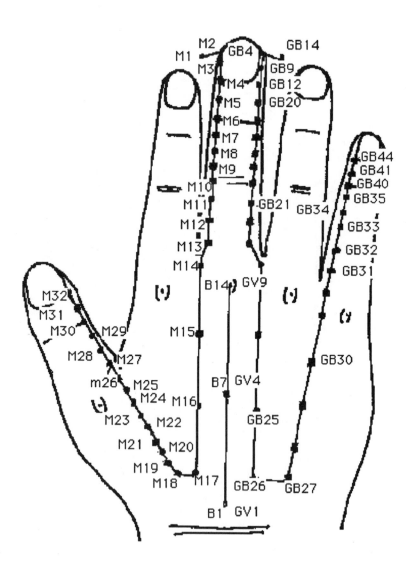

Gall Bladder Channel - body

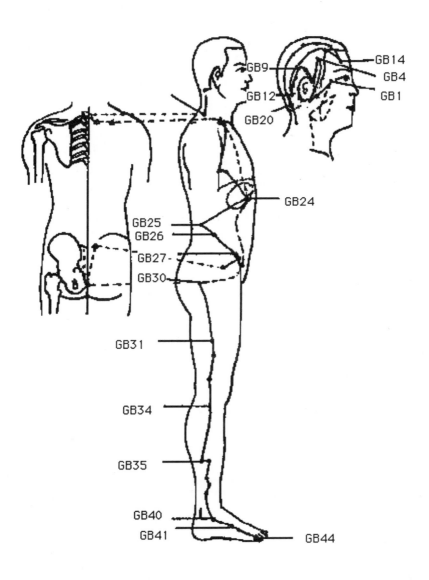

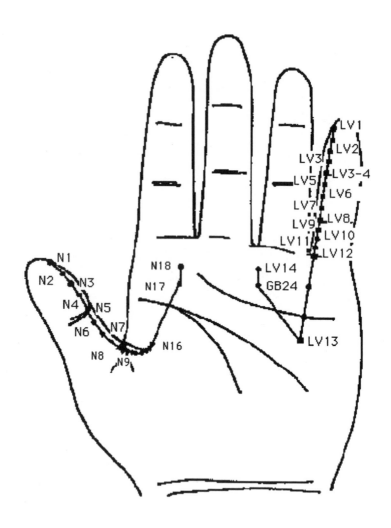

Liver Channel - body

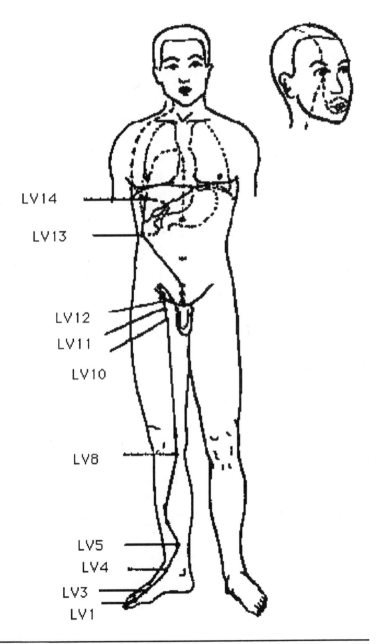

LV14

LV13

LV12

LV11

LV10

LV8

LV5

LV4

LV3

LV1

Conception Vessel - hand

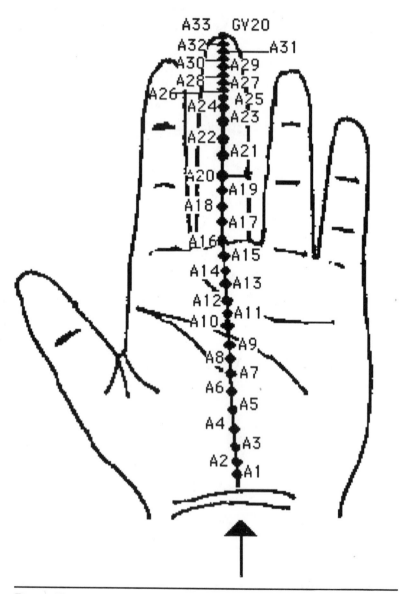

Conception Vessel - body

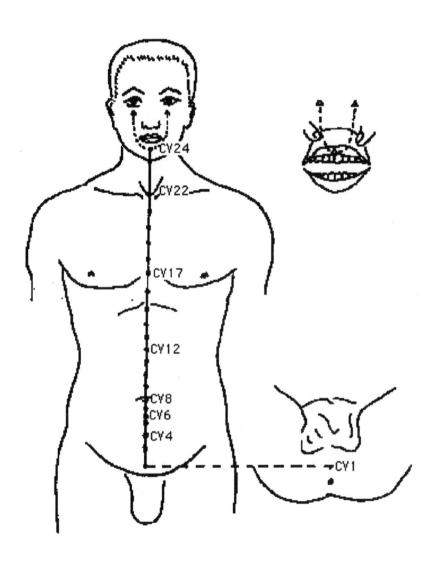

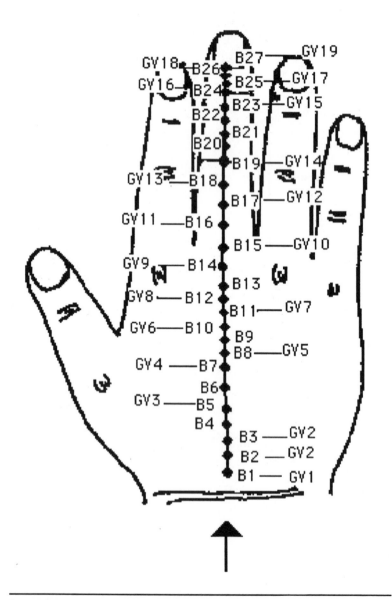

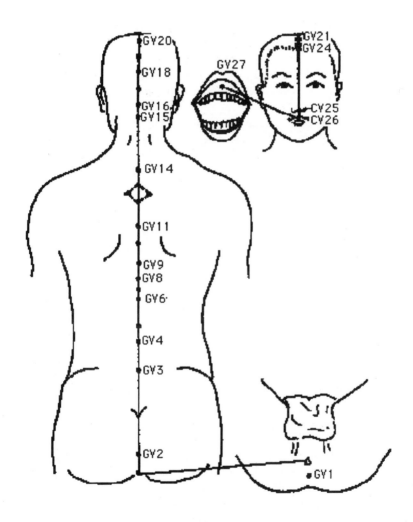

Meditation and Spiritual (Energetic) Development With Magnets

This is the subject that fascinates me the most regarding magnets, and an area in which magnets can be of inestimable value. The use of magnets in this field is an innovation whose time has truly come. Any brand of meditation, martial art, athletic endeavor or energetic path can benefit from regular use of magnets to balance and enhance development.

For the purposes of this discussion, we will equate meditation with spiritual, energetic and athletic development systems, although many do not strictly use meditation. To excel in any of these fields, balance on many levels is important and magnets are a valuable means to that end.

Meditation basically involves attaining a state of mind (or "no mind") that facilitates a particular energy flow in the body. The many methods achieving this body/mind harmony include sitting in various positions, breathing in specific patterns, concentrating on different body areas, repeating special words, and a multitude of visualization techniques. The bottom line is that all of the various mental or physical techniques aim at either producing an energetic effect on the body to help put the mind in a particular state or trying to put the mind in a particular state that will produce a specific energetic effect on the body.

We already know that magnets can be used to influence the energy channels of the body, why not use them specifically to augment various meditative and energetic practices?

I do not believe for one moment that the elusive state of "enlightenment" can be attained by taping magnets to the hand or body. Enlightenment comes from long years of work harmonizing body and mind, until through that union spirit manifests as light and body, mind, and spirit are one. Even this stage is just a beginning — the Chi is infinite.

In any case, any tool that aids this process is worth acquiring and utilizing if it is not antagonistic to the path you have chosen. When properly understood and utilized, magnets are an extremely powerful tool to aid in the energetic development of the being. They can be used in conjunction with most other practices to offer an added inducement to the body's energy to flow in a manner that will augment the thrust of that practice. To use this tool to improve one's health and the efficiency of one's energetic practice one must understand the energetic purpose of the practice and find the correct correct Magnet Mantra (placement of magnets on the body) to use this tool as a means to better health and more efficient energetic development.

Most schools of spiritual practice believe that the life force, when activated by their practices, can and will heal the physical, mental, and emotional states of man as well as develop the spiritual side of his being. In fact, most schools maintain that better overall health results from following their particular path. They encourage better health.

This alone is a good motivation to use magnets in combination with your practice—the more you can straightened out your body energetics from the outside, the less the energy generated from your practice will have to cope with these imbalances and the more it will be able to concentrate on the more subtle aspects of your spiritual development.

Simply improving your health is a big step towards progressive spiritual development. Meditation is theoretically healing to the physical body as whatever correct method you are using will facilitate the natural flow of energy in your body. If you meditate with an arrangement of magnets aimed at balancing your energetic body taped to your hands, the magnets should help your meditation and your meditation should help the magnets.

If fact, persons should magnetically address the gross physical imbalances before magnetically directing the energy towards purely spiritual goals. In most cases, since body, mind and spirit are one, the Magnetic Mantra will work at all levels simultaneously— maximizing the effect on your health and spiritual development. Once the physical body is in a reasonably balances state, one may specifically direct the Magnetic Mantra at more subtle spiritual/energetic goals.

The energetic goals of specific practices are different and there are a number of techniques available to approach each one.

For instance, one might be dealing with a specific meditational technique to release anger. In Indian Yogic theory, anger could be associated with several of the Chakras. We could, through back-up diagnostic investigations, find out which Chakra was the most out of balance and work directly on that area. In Taoist energetic theory, anger is associated with an imbalance in the energy of the liver, so we could discover the nature of the imbalance through our diagnostic system and utilize Five Element Treatments as described in the chapter on Five Elements. Another valid approach would be to utilize the Eight Extraordinary Vessels through any of the diagnostic methods explained in the chapter on the Extraordinary Vessels.

Emotional blocks are often encountered in clinical practice and on the spiritual path. An understanding of this subject is vital for a practice in either field.

Taoist Theory

In Taoist Theory there are seven emotions classified with organ\element correspondences and five visceral entities classified with organ\element correspondences. These correspondences are as follows:

• **Wood**	liver	anger	Hun
• **Fire**	heart	joy	Shen
• **Earth**	stomach	pensiveness/reminiscence	I
• **Metal**	lungs	grief and worry	Po
• **Water**	kidneys	fear terror (shock/fright)	Chen

All of these emotions are a normal part of living in this world and the body is expected to experience them, it is when there is an excess or deficiency of any one of these emotions that pathology will result. Emotional imbalance will cause pathology in the energetics of the associated organ, and an imbalance in the energetics of an organ can cause emotional stress associated with the emotion of that organ. If the imbalance continues for a long period or it is very severe, the visceral entities can become involved signifying deep psychological problems.

The re-establishment of natural, harmonious emotional responses is one of the goals of most spiritual/energetic disciplines.

Emotional excesses or deficiencies affect the spirit/consciousness in adverse ways, (spirit/consciousness being the coordination of all impressions and responses of the body). Mental and physical confusion may result if its decisions are faulty due to lack of clear direction or unintelligible or contradictory perceptions. If, on the other hand, the spirit/consciousness is clear with a strong sense of purpose, it can often work through a distorted emotional climate.

The visceral entities are the spiritual part of man which reflect in his life attitudes and actions. The visceral entities are linked to various energetic areas of the body. They are connected through the Five Elements cycle just as the emotions, organs and other element associations are connected and can be treated with Five Element acupuncture techniques as explained in the chapter on Five Elements.

All five of the visceral entities must be present in sufficient quantity and proper relation to each other for man to act and think correctly. In a nutshell, "Hun" accumulates information, "I" ponders the information and "Shen" receives information from both sources and draws conclusions. "Chen" provides the will to act on the conclusions and "Po" controls the vehicle which manifests that action in the physical world.

"Shen" is the guiding spirit which directs the overall activities of the body and especially the other visceral entities. It is the central government of the entire body-mind-spirit complex. Part of "Shen" is acquired from our parents (genetically) and part is developed through information provided by "Hun" and "I". Shen coordinates and digests this information, thus growing from it. Residing in the Heart, Shen enjoys the physical sensations of life and can become addicted to emotions. Because Shen is so intimately connected to the emotions, a disharmony in any of them will quickly affect Shen and the Heart. The quality of our emotions and physical sensations are changed with the onslaught of illness of any kind and Shen will soon be attacked as will be evidenced by a lack of brightness in the eye and generally disturbed spirit.

In Taoist theory there are six Yin organs among the primary twelve organs and also six Yang organs. The Yin organs, being deeper by nature, are the residing places of the Visceral Entities. We have mentioned five Visceral Entities relating to five Yin organs. The sixth organ (or function) is the Pericardium and the physically manifested location is the fatty tissue surrounding the Heart. The pericardium has two functions: to protect the Heart, and to relate the orders of the Shen residing in the heart to the rest of the energetic and physical body. Attacks upon the Heart are first borne by the Pericardium and this holds true for both emotional and physical/energetic attacks. If the Pericardium is strong, the Heart/Shen will be protected. If the Shen is weak, the orders issued will be unclear and/or inappropriate and disaster the follow. A weak Shen will also be unable to order correctly the functioning of the Pericardium itself and allow the emotions or other energetic disturbances to directly access the heart. The heart and Pericardium are often used in both pathological and meditational therapy.

Joy is the emotion associated with the Heart. Too much Joy suspends the Spirit/consciousness in the upper burner. Essentially, this stagnation of energy will lead to stagnation of blood, and the formation of internal heat and internal wind. Exhaustion of fluids from the internal heat will lead to formation of phlegm and obstruction of the energy channels especially those of the heart. This condition can lead to hysteria, senseless talking, uncontrolled weeping and laughing, all sorts of mental derangement and coma. Severe or prolonged emotional excess or deficiency of any organs associated emotion will affect Shen, especially when the emotion pertains to the heart.

Po, the visceral entity of the lungs, directs the physical energies of the body, including blood, defensive energy, nutritive energy, motor reflexes, unlearned traits, hereditary characteristics, and many autonomic functions. Although many of the above-mentioned energies and substances are associated with one or more of the other organs in their physically manifested state, the spirit of the physical body as a whole is controlled by Po. In old China, corpses were buried eight days after death. Up until that time, the nails and hair would still grow signifying that Po was still functioning. The Po is the last of the visceral entity spirits to leave the body at death, the one least involved in reasoning and thinking, and the one most involved with the physical being. A long standing emotional problem with grief or worry will eventually affect Po.

Grief and worry are the emotions associated with the Lung. They are Yin and usually attack the Yang of the lung first, depressing the Spirit/Consciousness and robbing the body of physical vitality. Worry causes energy to stagnate and coagulate thereby blocking the channels. Worry brings disharmony to the lungs first, but through the mother-son relationship often affects the spleen also.

Sadness/grief affects the Lung energy differently. It breaks the flow and cohesion of energy allowing the energy to leak out of the body thus causing weakness. Grief can be caused externally by environmental/social conditions or internally by an excess of Yin or deficiency of Yang in any of the organs. Both grief and worry can cause respiratory problems of all kinds.

The conscious and subconscious thinking activities of the mind are directed by Hun, the visceral entity of the Liver. Hun has little to do with automatic physical energies (Po), but is directly involved with the collection of information from all of the experiences of the individual. Hun logs the information, sorts out the useful, and passes it on to the Shen. People who constantly fail to learn from experience have a problem with Hun. Dreams are the disturbed movement of Hun, thus dream disturbed sleep is treated through the liver.

Anger is the emotion associated with the Liver. Anger has an upward energetic movement which causes Spirit/Consciousness to be overabundant in the head and shoulders. Anger can be caused by unreasonableness and frustration with oneself and others. Highly critical, angry people often manifest health problems in the head such as sinus problems, headache, ringing of the ears, etc. Anger is a Yang emotion that damages the Yin-blood-(Liver stores blood) so Yin-blood deficient people often are subject of fits of anger. Weakened Yin-blood of the Heart (Heart is the master of blood) and Kidneys (kidneys store basic Yin and Yang of the body) can also lead to anger. The visceral entity of the Kidneys, Chen, is the controller of will and if Kidney Yin is weak Chen can cause stubbornness which leads to frustration and anger.

The Liver is in charge of the free flowing energy in all of the organs. If an emotional problem affects any organ it will disturb the free flow of energy in that organ and soon affect the liver. The Liver is often called the emotional organ for that reason.

Physical symptoms such as menstrual problems, headaches (especially at the Vertex), red eyes, tendon and ligament problems (Liver nourishes the tendons and ligaments), eye problems, etc. occur with liver disturbances.

The "I" is the visceral entity of the Spleen and is in charge of recollection. Thoughtless acts and obsessions are both symptoms of a disturbed "I".

Pensiveness or reminiscence is the emotion of the spleen. Excess reminiscence causes the Spirit/Consciousness to be concentrated in the brain. The Spirit/Consciousness considers past lessons through pensiveness, but excessive brooding causes energetic problems with the spleen and Heart (Shen). Deficient spleen symptoms, such as gastrointestinal problems, prolapses, menstrual and blood problems, abdominal distension, loss of energy, etc. will then occur.

Chen, the visceral entity of the Kidneys, controls will power and perseverance. When Chen is depleted, one is unable to follow through on plans and desires to put responsibility on others. This is commonly encountered on spiritual paths where the aspirant places the responsibility of his development on the teacher rather than on himself.

Fear and terror are the emotions associated with the kidneys and they cause the Spirit/Consciousness to descend to the bowels and lower extremities. The cause of these emotions can be from environmental effects or from a weakness of the kidney energy itself. When attacking the Kidney energy, these emotions usually deplete Kidney Yang first and then Kidney Yin. Since Kidney Yang is the main energy used to warm the body, cold symptoms such as edema, cold limbs, low back pain that is worse with cold, etc. will begin to appear. When Kidney Yin (which is in charge of bone marrow) is affected, symptoms like low back pain that is not sensitive to cold, ringing of the ears, night sweats, poor memory (Brain is marrow), etc. will appear.

It must always be kept in mind that many of the symptoms involved in the disorder of one organ may also be involved in disorders of other organs. Also, disorders of any one organ may cause disorders in other organs. The secondary disorder may manifest symptoms in the physical plane more prominently than the root imbalance.

When diagnosing emotional and Visceral Entity problems, we must remember that they fit into the Five Element Model. The same nourishing and control cycles exist at this level as at the organ level and can be utilized for both diagnosis and treatment.

The Visceral Entities can be harmed not only by excess or deficient emotional states but also by an excess or deficient implementation of the attributes they control.

For instance, Po can become excess if one performs repetitive tasks in a robot-like manner. There is a need for balance in one's life. If an athlete routinely trains many hours a day in a thoughtless manner, an imbalance will develop manifesting as an excess of Po. By the nourishing cycle this could feed the "son" entity (Chen) which is in charge of will and perseverance. This will result in more training. By the control cycle, the Hun would be overpowered which would not only limit the amount of information fed to Shen in the Heart, but also inhibit the proper screening of useful or useless information for the guiding spirit. Again by the control cycle, Shen in the Heart would be unable to control Po which would allow more of the training. By the nourishing cycle again, the "I" would be affected in one of two ways. It would either become deficient by having to feed Po too much, in which case the ability to reflect on conditions would be impaired, or it would become overfull or in excess by energy backing up from Po, in which case obsession would prevail and even more training would be the result.

This scenario is common, in varying degrees, in groups where individual thought is regarded as extraneous and lifestyle is very regimented. Any number of disharmony combinations is possible within the visceral entities. A careful evaluation should be made for each patient to discover the true energetic state of balance and what is needed to correct it.

Proper diet is very important in nourishing those organs which are deficient. Good diet guidelines can be found in numerous publications on Oriental Medicine.

As stated before, all these imbalances may be treated through the Five Element Therapies described in the chapter on that subject. I believe that treating the front and back alarm points for the organs is also very useful in these cases, being sure to have one north magnet and one south magnet in each pair of points and O-Ring testing to be sure the treatment is appropriate. Because Divergent Channel treatments work at such a deep level, I believe they are also extremely useful, especially in the magnet diagnosis presented in the chapter on divergent meridian treatments.

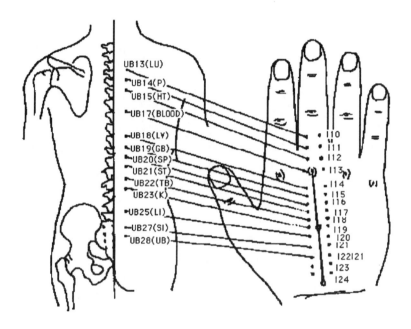

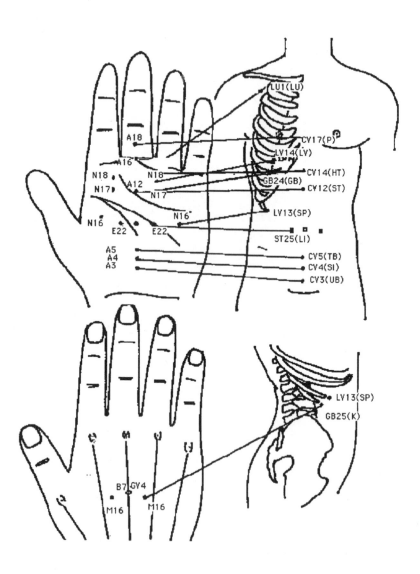

Most acupuncturists will be familiar with the Taoist view of body energetics since classical oriental medical theory uses that model. Aside from the Five Element, Divergent Meridian, and Alarm Point therapies already mentioned for emotional/physical/spiritual balancing, the Eight Extraordinary Vessels play a major part in spiritual work and indeed are sometimes called the Psychic Channels. It is absolutely necessary to clear the Extraordinary Vessels of all obstructions for the unimpeded flow of generative force and vital breath to take place. This circulation is a necessary for all higher development in the Taoist systems.

Abdominal diagnosis clearly shows which Extraordinary Vessels are obstructed and any of the diagnostic models and their corresponding treatments presented in the chapter on the Extraordinary Vessels, are valid therapies for meditational/spiritual balancing. Here again, the specific aim of the particular meditation used must be weighed against the actual physical/energetic health of the body complex in order to choose the best Magnet Mantra to use.

Indian Yoga

In Indian Yoga, the most popular energy system used for spiritual progress is the Chakra system. Chakras are assigned anatomical locations but represent areas or spheres of influence more than physical sites. Located along the course of the spinal column in ascending order of subtlety, they are centers of interchange between the physical and psychological energies of the body on the physical plane. It is at these centers that the activities of the life force interact with the sympathetic, and parasympathetic nervous systems. An imbalance in one or more of these Chakras is believed to be the root of all disease in the body, mind, spirit complex. In a Chakra, outgoing energy is the experience of activity and incoming energy is the experience of sensation.

There are seven main Chakras which are used for energetic development although many others are described. We will mention one of the minor Chakras within the sphere of the seventh or Crown Chakra later in this book. They begin at the base of the spine and ascend to the crown of the head, with the lower Chakras said to deal with grosser survival of the body energies and the higher Chakras dealing with the more spiritual and subtle aspects of existence.

In Taoist theory, the locations of the Chakras are recognized as powerful energy centers although the attributes assigned to them may not exactly correspond to Indian thought. The respective Taoist energy centers have traditional acupuncture points that are said to access these areas, and interestingly, each of the centers has a associated endocrine gland which can be accessed by that point and often many other points This lays the groundwork for a two point north/south magnet therapy to be applied to those areas.

The endocrine or ductless glands produce hormones which act as chemical messengers and ultimately affect all the cells of the body. The hormones are released directly into the bloodstream and either stimulate or suppress some phase of metabolism. The endocrine gland system operates on a complex feedback system which, when in proper balance, regulates the entire body/mind/spirit complex.

The Chakras may not be glands as such, but the endocrine glands are certainly extremely powerful manifestations of the basic Chakra energy. Helping to regulate the specific glands is one way to help regulate the Chakra energy.

The Taoist view these glands as an interconnecting and interdependent system of energy production and storage in the body. A weakness in any one gland will weaken all the glands and to maintain proper function of one all must be functioning in proper order.

I believe this interdependent and interconnecting theory applies to the Chakras also. Many people want to have their "Third Eye" opened with external intervention yet they are depleted in other areas. With such a person we would be doing them a real disservice by concentrating on what they think they want rather than on what our diagnostic skills tell us they need. The Magnet Mantras can help the energy centers to balance and provide a fertile environment for spiritual work to be accomplished but they cannot do the work for anyone nor can they force spiritual awakenings before the proper time. Any such attempt would lead to much more harm than help.

In the following pages, I will describe one minor and seven major Chakras, their Indian associations, the endocrine gland associated with each Chakra, the master acupuncture points for the Chakra, and several acupuncture points directly associated with the glands. The master point of the Chakra and one of the points associated with the gland within the Chakra is one way to balance the Chakra locally. The Eight Extraordinary Vessels have extremely powerful effects of the endocrine system and can be used both for local and overall Chakra balancing.

Muladhara Chakra   Foundation Root Center
Taoist Name: House of Essence

The location of this Chakra is said to be the base of the spine, pelvic plexes, the first three vertebra, and the region between the anus and the genitals. It has the slowest rate of energetic vibration of the seven main Chakras (each Chakra vibrates at a rate higher than those below it and lower than those above it). It represents the earth element which stands for solidity and security. All solid aspects of the body including bones, nails, teeth, etc. are said to be controlled by this energy center. Muladhara represents physical birth, the physical plane, and security and satisfaction in one's state of being. The color associated with the first Chakra is yellow, its work organ is the anus, its sense organ is the nose, and its sense relationship is to smell. The shape associated with this Chakra is the square, and its basic concerns are food and shelter.

Meditation on the top of the nose is one method of accessing Muladhara which is the seat of Kundalini in the human body, the root of all growth and awareness of the divinity of man.

Kundalini is the dormant spiritual energy coiled about the base of the spine. The human mind and body can function in the physical plane without arousing the unlimited energy source, but to progress on the spiritual path of energetic development and God-consciousness this energy must be aroused and controlled in an ascent through each of the Chakras.

The energy within Muladhara controls the expulsion of semen from the male, the child from the mothers womb, and urine in both sexes. The energy in this Chakra is neutral, leaving it up to man as to what use it will be given. The overall creative force is the energy ruling this center and sexual energy is the most powerful manifestation of this force.

When energized, this Chakra promotes the beginning of awareness, patience, freedom from disease, stamina, vigor, vitality, security, an understanding of inner purity and the desire for more experience and information. When energetically out of balance, Muladhara can foster violent behavior based on insecurity, illusion, greed, anger, delusion, avarice and unbalanced sensuality.

The first Chakra is concerned with survival and relates to birthplace, culture, early relationships and the manifestation of material possessions. In early life it is nurtured by love from the outside and those lacking early love often have a deficiency here.

Weakness in the first Chakra can lead to lack of confidence and direction, the inability to achieve goals self destructive tendencies, weakness and low sex drive. Stuck energy in this energy can lead to egotistic, greedy, domineering behavior with addictions to wealth, power, and sex.

The sex glands are associated with the first Chakra. There are three major acupuncture points that control this area:

Governing Vessel 1 (B1) - Long Strength - is located in a hollow at the proximal end of the wrist bones on the back side of the hand. In body acupuncture, it is called Chang Chiang and is located between the tip of the coccyx and the anus. The traditional functions are "to open the Conception and Governing Vessels and to regulate the intestines" (O'Connor and Bensky, p.216)

Conception Vessel 1 (A1) is located 5mm distal to the central part of the wrist joint. In body acupuncture, it is called Hui-Yin - reunion of Yin, gate of mortality, door of life and death - and is located on the perenium midway between the scrotum or vulva and the anus. This point directly influences the Bulbourethral gland and the testes.

The testes are the generative and reproductive glands of the male. They secrete sperm and the male energizing force. They help regulate the strength and stability of the bones through their influence on calcium absorption and influence secondary sex characteristics. Some other acupuncture points that strongly affect the testes are DU 3,4; CV 3,4,7; KI 7, 10, 11; ST 29, 30: UB 52, 54; and the Extraordinary Vessel pairs of UB 62/ SI 3 and LU 7/ KI 6.

Conception Vessel 3 (A3) is located one third of the way between CV1 (A1) and CV 8 (A8) on the hand and four units directly below the navel on the body. Its traditional functions are "to assist the transforming function of the chi, regulate the uterus, and alleviate damp heat." (O'Connor and Bensky, p.180) Its Chinese name means middle summit or middle pole. It is also called sperm palace and directly influences the uterus, prostate and seminal vesicle.

The uterus has a possible endocrine function not fully under- stood, but it is known to relate directly to the nervous system and posterior pituitary. Some other acupuncture points that strongly affect the uterus are SP 8, 6; KI 9; GB 26.

The prostate gland stores seminal fluid and also has a little understood connection to the nervous system. It secretes an alkaline fluid that becomes part of the seminal fluid. Some acupuncture points that strongly affect this gland are SP 6, 9: UB 23, 28; KI 12; ST 28, 29; and CV2, 4.

The seminal vesicles are two sack-like glands lying behind the urinary bladder that secrete a thick lubricating fluid that becomes part of the semen. They can be affected by the same acupuncture points that relate to the prostate gland.

Svadisthana Splenic Chakra   Sacral Center
Taoist Name: House of Water

The second Chakra is located in the area of the sacrum, splenic
plexus, and hypogastric plexus and relates to the element water.
It controls fluidity and ripeness in the body and dominates
urine, saliva, semen and other body fluids. The energy of the
second Chakra deals with sexuality (especially emotionally),
family relationships, sense of self worth, creativity, emotions,
intuition, friendships and is influenced by the way emotions
were expressed or repressed in childhood.

The first and second Chakras are both concerned with sexuality.
The testes—seat of the generative force in the male—are located
in the first Chakra (Muladhara) and the ovaries, seat of the
generative force in the female, are located in the second
(Svadisthana) Chakra. This explains why in many cases the
male sexuality is expressed on a more physical plane and the
female sexuality is expressed on a more emotional plane.

Svadisthanas' color is light blue, its shape is the circle (moon)
and itssense is taste. The tongue is the sense organ and the
genitals are the work organ of the second Chakra. It is associated with the astral plane and the moon, which affects both
ocean tides and the menstrual cycle. Purity, friendliness,
optimism, creativity, imagination and a full sense of humor are
attributes of this Chakra. It is here that the outward expansion
of personality begins. Svadisthana is also the seat of basic
intuition, fantasy, cunning and the inspiration to create.

Meditation on this Chakra enables one to reflect the world as a
lake reflects the sun, and to use creative energy to refine artistic
endeavors and personal relationships.
Congested energy in this center can foster anger, lust, jealousy,
aggressiveness, irritation, greed, false perceptions of reality and
manipulative behavior.

Congested energy in the second Chakra can lead to feelings of
low self esteem, impotence on both physical and mental levels,.
fearfulness, paranoia and shutting down on many levels. The
glands associated with the second Chakra are the ovaries (and

mammaries by energetic connection, not anatomical location) and Kidneys. The main acupuncture points controlling this center are governing vessel 4 and 8. Some authorities place the female sex organs and Conception Vessel 4 in the first Chakra.

Conception Vessel 4 is located three sevenths of the way from A1 (CV1) to A8 (CV8) on the hand and three units directly below the navel on the body. Its traditional functions are "to nourish and stabilize the Kidneys, regulate the Chi, and restore the Yang." (O'Connor andBensky, p.185)

The spleen is associated with the second Chakra. This organ aids digestion, directly absorbs solar energy, and stores vital energy to stimulate the body, fight disease and purify the system. The spleen is also involved in the destruction of old red blood cells. It is directly affected by CV 10, UB 20, and LIV 13.

Governing Vessel 4 is located halfway between B1 (GV1) and B14 (GV 9) on the hand and between the second and third lumbar vertebra on the body. Its Chinese name is Ming Men - Life Door - and has the traditional functions of "nourishing the source Chi, strengthening the Kidneys and benefitting the lumbar vertebrae." (O'Connor and Bensky, p. 208)

The mammary glands are involved in the production of milk and have an endocrine function that orders and normalizes menstruation. Some acupuncture points that strongly affect the mammary glands are HE 1; SI 1: UB 51: GB 41, 42: ST 34, 18, 16, 15, 14; CV 17.

The kidney contains endocrine cells which produce blood pressure elevating substances and red blood cell production stimulators. It is the storehouse of the basic Yin/Yang of the body. UB 23 and GB 25 directly access the kidneys. Other points which strongly affect the Kidney/Adrenal complex are SP 6, 2: CV 10, 16; KI 6, 7; GV 4, 6, 10, 11, 13, 17, 26; and UB 52.

The adrenals, which GV 4 also affects, are located just above the kidneys. They contain an inner medulla and an outer cortex. The cortex originates from the same tissue as the sex glands and has a strong effect on the secondary sex characteristics The adrenal secretion, adrenaline, energizes the muscles and is the biological stimulus for the Fight or Flight reaction. Other adrenal secretions influence carbohydrate, lipid and protein metabolism, blood saline content and blood pressure, concentration of blood glucose, heart and respiration rate, body temperature, digestive motility, and overall mental and physical responsiveness.

Mental or physical excess, stress, poor diet, and living beyond our biological and spiritual means all undermine the adrenal functions. This can leave us in a continual state of body/mind/spirit depletion and disharmony.

Manipura Chakra The City of Gems   Solar Center
Taoist Name: House of Transcendence

The third Chakra is located at the level of the epigastric and solar plexus in the spine. It is associated with the element fire, with expansiveness, warmth, and joviality. The sense associated with this Chakra is sight, with the eyes being its sense organs and the feet and legs being its work organs. The third Chakra is associated with the celestial plane. Light is ruled by this center. Insight, intuition and the light in which we see ourselves and the world, depend upon the strength of this fire element. Visualization is an important aspect of this Chakra. The fire of passion springs from this center and that passion can be manifested in shape, ideas, concepts, etc. The shape associated with this Chakra is the triangle.

The assimilation of food through combustion is controlled through Manipura and hunger, thirst, sleep and body energy are strongly influenced here. This is also the center of a person's conscious thought and personal centeredness.

Congested energy in this Chakra can lead to compulsive behavior, rashness, desire for fame and power, and excess critical and dominant behavior. Weakness in the Manipura Chakra energy causes one loss confidence in oneself, depression, distrust of others, poor assimilation of food, and excessive worry.

Proper energizing brings the power to organize and command, speak well, realize fantasies, cure digestive and bowel problems, accept new challenges, and develop new skills.

The adrenals and pancreas relate to the third Chakra. CV 12, and GV 6 are the controlling acupuncture points for this area.

Conception Vessel 12 is located midway between A 8 (CV 8) and A 16 (CV 14) on the hand and four units above the umbilicus on the body. Its Chinese name means Middle Palace or Middle Cavity. It relates to the pancreas gland and in Chinese Medicine is the master point for all the Yang organs. Its traditional function is "to regulate the stomach chi and transform and suppress rebellious chi." (O'Connor and Bensky, p. 179)

Governing Vessel 6 (Chichung) is located three sevenths of the way from B7 (GV 4) to B 14 (GV 9) on the hand and between the eleventh and twelfth thoracic vertebrae on the body. It directly influences the adrenals. Governing Vessel 4 also influences the adrenals as explained before.

The pancreas produces pancreatic juice which plays an important role in the digestion of all types of food. It also produces insulin and glycogen which are of primary importance in regulating carbohydrate metabolism. The pancreas is also strongly affected by CV 11; KI 3; LIV 2; ST 36, 40; and UB 21.

Anahata Unstricken/Unbeaten   Heart Center
Taoist Name: House of Heart

Anahata, the Heart Center, is located on the spine at the level of the heart, cardiac plexus, and breastbone. It is associated with air, dwells in the chest, and is tasteless, odorless, colorless, and formless. It is in this center that the more physical elements from below and the spiritual elements from above are harmonized. It is also here that psychic and spiritual experience may begin to take place. The sense associated with the fourth Chakra is touch, its sense organ is the skin, and its work organ is the hand. The associated shape is the hexagram and the colors may be smoky gray or green, pink, or it can be colorless. The sense of touch can be interpreted on the physical, emotional, or spiritual levels. Compassion is an important attribute of this center.

The plane of Anahata is balance. This center tries to balance not only the three centers above with the three centers below, but also the outside world with the inside world. Meditation on this Chakra can produce divine vision, awareness of karma, love, faith, and devotion. The inner guide expresses itself through the Heart Chakra, whose energy is self generating. An inner strength may be developed here that will transcend ordinary reality.

Congested energy in this center can cause restlessness, spiritual confusion, possessiveness, manic-depressive behavior and a critical, demanding attitude. Weak energy in this center leads to loss of direction, self pity, fears of all types, and a sense of being out of touch with oneself and one's path. The gland associated with Anahata Chakra is the Thymus. CV 17 is the controlling point for this Chakra.

Conception Vessel 17 - Shan Chung (Middle of the chest or Gentlemen's Palace) is located halfway between A 16 (CV 14) and A 20 (CV 22) on the hand and at the central point between the nipples on the body. The traditional functions are "to suppress rebellious chi, expand the chest and benefit the diaphragm" (O'Connor and Bensky, p. 177). The energy of all the meridians concentrates at this point. Some other points that directly affect the thymus are CV 12 to 21; SP 2; UB 11: and GB 34.

The thymus dominates the growth of children before puberty and at about the ages of 11 to 14 it begins to regress slowly and continues to do so throughout life. The thymus has a great influence on the lymphatic system and is important in the sexual differentiation of male and female. In some Taoist Yoga practices the correct mixing of the energy from the thymus, pituitary and sex glands is used to prolong life by reversing or slowing down the aging process.

Vishuddha   Pure   Throat Center
Taoist Name: House of Growth

Vishuddha, the throat center, is located at the level of the
carotid plexus and pharyngeal plexus. It is associated with the
element ether and embodies the quality of space. This center is
the melting pot from which the other four elements arise and to
which they return. It is a bridge through which the Brow
Chakra controls the four lower Chakras. Knowledge and
communication are the principal aspects of the fifth Chakra,
smoky purple is its color and the crescent is its associated
shape. The work organ associated with Vishuddha is the
mouth, its sense organ is the ear, and hearing is its sense. This
Chakra is the center of sound in the body. It symbolizes purity,
one of its major energetic functions is to purify the body.

Vishuddha refines the elements of the four lower Chakras:
cooling liquids and foods to make them palatable, and governing
psychic energy, clairvoyance and wordless communication. This
Chakra is the center of dreams in the body, and controls past
memories of the lore of nature, especially plant lore. Its energy
promotes patience, self-consciousness, memory in general, wit,
intuition, improvisation and oneness with nature.

Meditation on the hollow of the throat is said to produce calm-
ness, serenity, purity, a good command of speech and pleasant
voice. The abilities to interpret dreams, communicate spiritual
sciences, and write poetry emanate from this center.

Congested energy in the fifth Chakra can lead to the unwise use
of knowledge, addictions, loud and excessive talking, and a
condescending attitude. Weak energy here causes one to lack
expressiveness, be overly shy, seek solitude and be fearful.

The thyroid and parathyroid glands are associated with the fifth
Chakra and the center is controlled by CV 21 and CV22. The
thyroid gland originates from the same area and, in fact, same
tissue as the anterior lobe of the pituitary gland. It is an energy
producing gland and influences the metabolism, growth and
stamina of the whole body. The thyroid helps build brain and
nerves and is a link between the brain and the sexual organs.

The thyroid is so closely linked in to the sexual organs that sexual arousal, menstruation and pregnancy directly affect it. In the evolutionary past, this gland allowed certain sea animals to dwell on land. It controls our speed of living.

The thyroid is absolutely necessary for the development and evolvution of psychic and mental powers and higher states of consciousness.

Just as the pituitary keeps the amount of salt in our blood proportional to the amount of salt in sea water, the thyroid keeps the amount of iodine in our blood proportionate to the amount of iodine in sea water, helping to balance the physical, mental, emotional and spiritual selves. Thyroid secretion stimulates gastric peristalsis and all metabolic processes and also aids in the detoxification of the body.

The parathyroids, which lie in or near the thyroid, help control calcium metabolism and aid in detoxifying the body. They play an important part in the health of nerves and muscles.

Conception Vessel 21 (Hsuan-Chi - North Star - Twelve Story) has no direct hand acupuncture point, so A 19 is used instead. On the body, CV 21 lies on the midline of the sternum about 1/2 unit below the suprasternal notch.

Conception Vessel 22 (Heaven's Prominence) is located 1/2 unit above the suprasternal notch in a depression on the midline. This point is A 20 in hand acupuncture and is located in the center of the second knuckle of the middle finger. The tradi-tional functions of this point are to "facilitate and regulate the movement of lung chi, cool the throat and clear the voice." (O'Connor and Bensky, p.174-176)

Other points that affect the thyroid are LI 11; ST 9, 10; SI 7; UB 15: GB 21: KI 7: TB 4, 5: DU 14, 24, 20: CV 6, 13, 22. Other points that affect the parathyroid are ST 36; UB 58, 11; DU 2.

Ajna   Authority/Command   Unlimited Power
Taoist Name: House of Intelligence

Ajna, the brow center, is located between the eyebrows at the
level of the medulla plexus and pineal plexus. Also known as
the Third Eye, it is the organ of clairvoyance symbolizing both
the basic Yin/Yang polarity of the body and the concept of non-
duality. The element of the sixth Chakra is the pure essence of
all the other elements, its color is transparent, luminescent
bluish or camphor white and its planes are austerity and
penance.

Ajna is the seat of psychic powers, higher intuition and the
mind/soul. This Chakra commands and controls the lower self.

Meditation on this center will eradicate all sins and impurities,
bring knowledge of past lives and the future, and place the
adept beyond all desires with no danger of backsliding. The
adept will be able to control breath and mind, generate scrip-
tures, and understand the inner meaning of cosmic knowledge.
The divine within will be revealed and the divine in others
reflected.

Congested energy in this Chakra may lead to egotistical and
maniacally authoritative behavior, while weakness may lead to
oversensitivity and lack of discipline.

The pituitary gland is associated with Ajna, sometimes called
"the conductor of the endocrine orchestra."(Jeynes p. 151) The
acupuncture point associated with this center is Yin Tang.
The pituitary gland lies at the base of the brain behind the root
of the nose. It is comprised of two distinct parts or lobes, the
anterior lobe and the posterior lobe. Each lobe has its own
embryological origin, history, functions and secretions in a
somewhat Yin/Yang - male/female relationship with its other
part.

The anterior pituitary originates in the mouth area and is the
master of the whole endocrine system. Secretions of the anterior lobe stimulate growth of bone and connective tissue and
stimulate the adrenal cortex, thyroid and production of breast

milk. they also influence pigment production in the skin. The anterior lobe helps balance the creative and sexual forces and skeletal growth.

The posterior pituitary develops from the oldest part of the nervous system. Here, as in the hypothalamus, we have a meeting of the endocrine and nervous systems. The posterior pituitary secretes hormones which control the salt and water content of the blood, raise blood pressure and stimulate plain muscle as in the uterus, gall bladder, ureter and urinary bladder. It also controls kidney secretions and the sugar content of both blood and urine. Sleep cycles, intellectual growth, and moral sense are influenced by the pituitary..

Yin Tang (Seal Hall, Gateway to Heaven, Original Cavity of the Spirit) is located at A 30 on the hand, and at the central point between the eyebrows on the body. Its traditional functions are to "eliminate wind heat and calm the spirit." (O'Connor and Bensky, p. 144.)

Other points that affect the pituitary are SP 6; UB 1, 60: GB 37; DU 11, 13, 15, 16, 17: CV 10, 16; KI 11, 13.

Sahasrara   Crown Chakra   Thousand Petaled
Taoist Name: House of Spirit

Sahasrara, the Crown Chakra, is located at the tip of the middle finger on the hand, A33, at the top of the cranium, and in the cerebral plexus on the body. Its plane is that of truth or reality. The seventh Chakra is the seat of the self, the luminescent soul, the essence of being.
When this center is successfully energized, immortality is realized — a state of no activity, no mind, no knowledge or knower, total liberation.

Congested energy in this Chakra can cause severe mental problems, headaches, and deep frustration. Weak energy in this center will lead to a lackluster existence.
Within Sahasrara is another minor Chakra called Soma Chakra (Nectar - the moon) which is located in the middle of the fore-

head on the body and at a 31 on the hand. This is a center for the realization of truth, beauty, and goodness. Meditation on this center will produce immortality in the physical body—youth, vitality, and victory over death, disease and decay.

The gland associated with Sahasrara is the pineal gland and the gland associated with Soma is the hypothalamus. The acupuncture point associated with the Crown Chakra is Governing Vessel 20, and the point for Soma is T'ien T'ing.

The pineal gland, or human compass, lies near the center of the brain. It is known as a bridge between the higher planes of consciousness and physical expression. That the pineal contains cells like the retina of the eye gives credence to the theory that it was an eye in past evolutionary times. It is the center of the highest spiritual cultivation. Some authorities place this gland in both the sixth and seventh Chakra.

The pineal gland acts with the adrenals in controlling skin pigmentation and the action of light on the skin pigment. It closely acts with the sex glands and brain to influence sexual development. At about the age of seven, the pineal begins to undergo involuntary changes. When fully developed, it shows us our path and manifests the guru within.

The hypothalamus is a link between the cerebral cortex and the pituitary gland. It has both a stimulating and inhibiting influence on the pituitary. The hypothalamus helps regulate energy through control of sleep, appetite, body temperature, sexual function and water balance. It also has a strong influence on our emotions and nervous system.

Governing Vessel 20, (Pai Hui/hundred meetings/yellow plain), relates to the pineal gland. It is located at A 33 on the tip of the middle finger on the hand and at the crown of the head on the body. The traditional functions of Pai Hui are to "clear the senses and calm the spirit, extinguish liver wind, and stabilize ascending Yang ." (O'Connor and Bensky, p. 141-142) GB 20 and UB 10 also strongly affect the pituitary.

T'ien T'ing is located at A 31 on the hand and in the middle of the forehead on the body. It relates to the hypothalamus which is also affected by GB 20 and UB 10.

The preceding information on the Chakras is not an attempt to produce a definitive work on the subject, nor to exhaust the field of endocrinology. It is a compilation of information from several sources, designed to give a general spirit-description of the energy centers, interconnections, and traits and to introduce some of the acupuncture points therapeutically useful in their balancing. As in most fields, authorities differ on just about every aspect of the Chakras —from color associations to gland involvements. I believe that the practitioner should be able to work within the frame of reference of the patient for most therapies aimed at energetic development. There are many ways to view body energetics—a careful evaluation of the patient's needs should produce a therapy acceptable to both practitioner and patient.

In therapy, we must remember to always use balance with the magnets (north and south magnet equal numbers) and to O-ring test each combination. The main acupuncture points described here are not the only points useful, but form a good guideline for choosing points. The points listed have many other uses in traditional Oriental Medicine.

We must also remember that the Chakras can be viewed as not only residing in the spine, but also extending horizontally to the front of the body. Choosing a point on the front and the back of the hand at the horizontal level of the Chakra is a very valid way of approaching direct Chakra therapy.

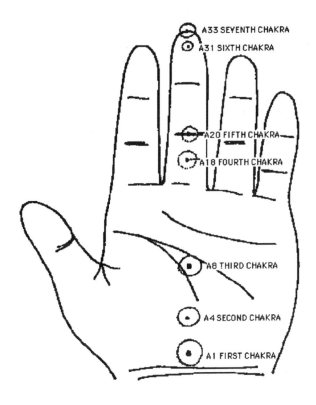

A33 SEVENTH CHAKRA
A31 SIXTH CHAKRA
A20 FIFTH CHAKRA
A18 FOURTH CHAKRA
A8 THIRD CHAKRA
A4 SECOND CHAKRA
A1 FIRST CHAKRA

The Eight Extraordinary Vessels are a very good way to deal with Chakra problems. They do not pinpoint any one Chakra, but have a very strong balancing action on the whole system. Problems with one Chakra must affect the others anyway, so it is not often that direct single Chakra therapy is needed. Theallowing the body to tell us which Vessels to use by abdominal palpation and showing us if our choice was correct upon rechecking the abdomen after the magnets have been applied by exhibiting the correct changes.

In Dr, Manakas' lecture, mentioned earlier, he stated that through experiments on rabbits ears, he found that an acupuncture needle caused the same affect whether inserted by a Master or a monkey. I believe that he was correct in the realm of measurable physiology, but I also believe that forces are at work that are beyond our ability to measure. I think that the spiritual intent of the practitioner does affect the outcome of the therapy and even more so in energetic development therapy.

The same is true with magnets. When they are placed on the hand, by yourself or by a practitioner, they have a specific effect in the physiological worlds. I believe that other effects can also be initiated depending upon how you arrived at the combination you are using and how you treat the therapy yourself. There are infinite variables involved in this concept and I will mention two important ones.

The development of your practitioner will affect the result of your therapy. The spiritual intent of your practitioner will carry over into your treatment on an energetic level and in the case of the Magnet Mantra, will continue to affect the quality of your experience as long as you use that particular method. This does not mean that you must have a levitating master as a practitioner to get good results, but bear in mind that the more developed your practitioner is the better your results are likely to be. If you plan to use magnets as an aid to energetic development, and use a practitioner in the process, try to find one that you know has been working on himself for a long time, that you feel very comfortable with and that appears to lead a healthy, balanced life.

Local and Superficial Techniques

Local treatment is covered in detail in Doctor Yoo's book and will be briefly overviewed here.

The most basic approach for correlative therapy is similar to ear acupunctur, in that a system of hand points corresponding to body parts is used But, since in hand acupuncture we have an actual meridian system, the other techniques of traditional body acupuncture can be used—distal points, meeting points, cleft points, and other special points.

Second, Doctor Yoo has introduced a triple burner therapy that is extremely useful for augmenting any other therapy. The triple burner therapy presented by Doctor Yoo can be used to augment any other therapy being used. As we know, the body is divided into three burning spaces: the upper burner, including the head, chest, upper back and arms; the middle burner, including the mid abdomen, mid back region; and the lower burner, including the lower abdomen, lower back and legs. Broadly speaking, the functions of the upper burner are respiration and blood circulation (lung and heart), the middle burner controls the digestive process (stomach, spleen, liver and gall bladder) and the lower burner controls the genitourinary systems (kidney, urinary, bladder).

Each burning space has a set of points used to strengthen its overall area of responsibility and function. The upper burner uses CV 14, CV 17 and CV 22. The middle burner uses CV 8, CV 12 and CV 14. The lower burner uses CV 1, CV 3 and either CV 8 or CV 12 for men and CV 1, CV 4, CV 5, CV 8 and CV 12 for women.

To strengthen the therapeutic effect of any treatment, the corresponding points of the problematic burner area can be stimulated. According to Doctor Yoo, moxibustion works best on the lower burner and pre made moxa stickers can be given to the patient for home use. The male and female lower burner treatments can thus be used as general tonics for the patient as can the middle burner points be used for digestive tract tonic. If

there is a problem with the digestive tract, that problem must
be dealt with first, as the healing energy of the whole body is
dependent upon proper functioning of this system. If there are
digestive problems, no matter what area the local problem is in,
the middle burner must be treated.

Triple Burner

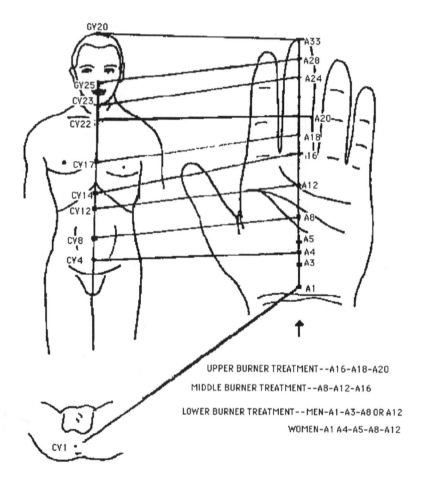

UPPER BURNER TREATMENT--A16-A18-A20

MIDDLE BURNER TREATMENT--A8-A12-A16

LOWER BURNER TREATMENT--MEN-A1-A3-A8 OR A12

WOMEN-A1 A4-A5-A8-A12

In the following illustrations, you will see which specific body areas correspond to the areas of the hand. The correlations are quite straightforward and the body meridians and the hand meridians cover approximately the same areas in the flow patterns.

Body/Hand Correspondences

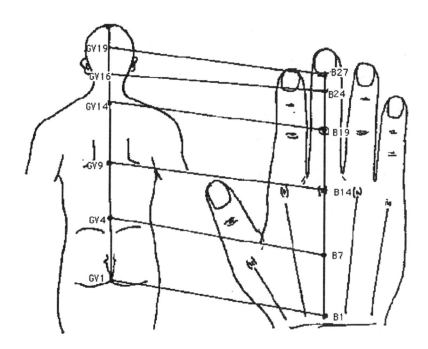

Body/Hand Correspondences

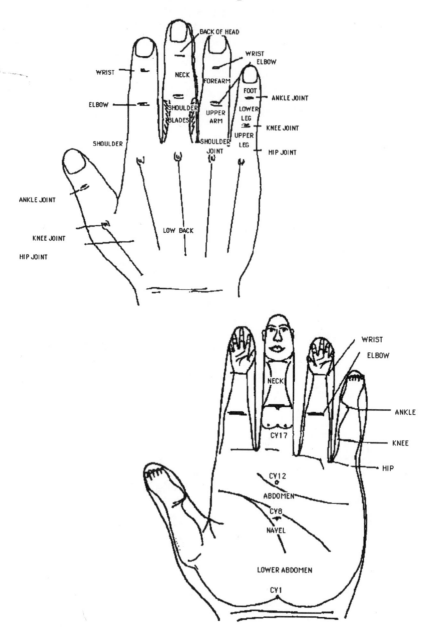

Doctor Yoo's published local area magnet therapy consists of finding the most sensitive spot in the area of the hand that corresponds to the troubled area of the body and placing a north magnet on that spot. In most cases, this works very well, but there are other techniques that I find work even better.

On page 175 of _Extraordinary Vessels_, Kiiko Matsumoto and Steven Birch present three principals of using the north/south polarities of magnets for treatment of local area problems.

These principals work equally well for hand acupunctureand-body acupuncture. I use the 600 gause Korean Hand Magnets rather that the 3000 gause magnets referred to in the following quote:

> "1. Treat the reactive area directly with the (N) 3000 and a point reflecting that area with the (S) 3000.
> 2. Treat the reactive area according to a left-right balance.
> 3. Treat the reactive area with the (N) 3000 and use the (S) 3000 further downstream on the same meridian to drain the reactive area."

The first principle simply means to use a north magnet on the painful/problem area and a south magnet on a related point in the energetic concept of Oriental Medicine. You may use any of the classical associations and muscle test to see if they are appropriate. Magnets work very quickly and in most cases the patient will notice a reduction in sensitivity at the reflex area within minutes. For example, shoulder pain may be treated with a north magnet on the local area of pain (on the local shoulder area of the hand) and a south magnet on large intestine 10 (of the hand) or any other point that relates to the shoulder, such as a distal point of the effected channel, or GB 34, the master point of tendons. Any point logical according to traditional Oriental Medical theory may be used. Always muscle test to be sure that the therapy is good for the patient and check for pain relief. If the right points are chosen, the muscle test should be strong and the pain should lessen.

If the pain is not relieved, try another logical point, even if the muscle test is strong. Perhaps the point you have chosen is logical and "good" but there may be a more effective point to use.

With hand acupuncture, it is very convenient to probe for reactive points, apply north magnets and search for other logical points to place the south magnet. If the points are correctly chosen, the pain will always change quite quickly and the muscle test will increase in strength. Take the time to find the correct spot.

The second principle simply means to put a north magnet on the reactive spot and a south magnet on the same spot on the opposite hand. For instance, left knee pain can be treated by placing a north magnet on the reactive point for the knee area on the left hand and a south magnet on the same point of the other hand.

The third principle is self explanatory. The north magnet is placed on the reactive area and the south magnet is placed at a reactive point downstream from the north magnet. The south magnet can be placed quite close to the north, just be sure to muscle test and observe a reduction in the pain at the reaction point.

On pages 266 and 267 of *Extraordinary Vessels* another interesting use of north/south magnets is presented. This is the theory of placing the magnets topographically opposite each other: again with the north on the reactive/painful spot and the south directly opposite. This is similar to the through and through needle technique we all know and love so much. I believe the Manaka Ion Beam Machine has a similar effect as the beam travels from one probe to another on the opposite side of the hand.

Many of us are familiar with the Akabane Technique in which small intradermal needles are inserted in the back shu points and allowed to remain for several days to several weeks. This very powerful method of therapy is in widespread use in Japan. The treatment point.to be used is chosen by intellect, palpation or a system of heating the endpoints of the meridian of the fingers and toes to find out which one is the least heat sensitive or which left/right pair is the most out of balance. The back of the hand contains all of the organ shu points and can be needled with either a traditional intradermal needle or an ear tack. In my experience, this therapy works very well and gives results equivalent to the back shu points. As this is very potent therapy, you must be sure to warn the patient about needle sickness. With the needle in the back of the hand it is easier for the patient to remove it than if it were in the traditional back shu point.

Back Alarm Points

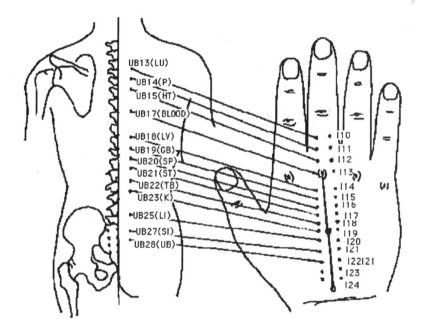

This therapy is very useful with any of the Eight Extra Meridians or Five Element treatments discussed later. Apply this therapy after other therapies and have patient retain needle 1 to 3 days!

When dealing with a single meridian and/or pain problem, it is often advantageous to leave a tonification or sedation treatment taped to the patient's hand. This allows the patient to get continuous pain relief or therapeutic stimulation. As we know, magnetic energy flows from north to south and affects meridian energy. The best place to affect the meridian energy with magnets is at the distal and middle joints of the fingers, along the course of the meridian we wish to influence—so we tape our magnets to these areas. If we want to sedate, we put the south magnet towards the origin of the meridian and the north magnet downstream. If we want to tonify, we put the north magnet towards the origin of the meridian and the south magnet downstream from the magnet.

Tonification and Sedation

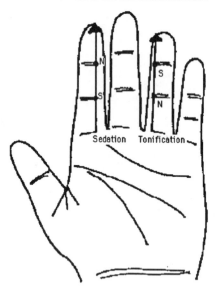

As always, muscle test after the magnets are in place. These arrangements of magnets are also the diagnostic method for finding the meridian imbalance. By placing the bar magnet (explained in the chapter on magnets) along the course of the meridian between the distal and middle joints, first in the sedation mode and muscle testing, and then in the tonification mode and muscle testing, we can ascertain the relative excess or deficiency of the meridian. If the meridian is deficient, the muscle test will be weak in the sedation mode and strong in the tonification mode. If the meridian is in excess, the muscle test will be strong in the sedation mode and weak in the tonification mode.

In his lectures, Leuk De Schepper refers to two other interesting techniques for pain control as the big shot and small shot techniques. The small shot technique is used for pain at one spot along a meridian. On the painful side, locate the first regular acupuncture point above or upstream from the pain, and place a north magnet on it. Then locate the first regular hand acupuncture point below or downstream from the painful spot and sedate it with a north magnet. Finally, on the painful side put a north magnet on the painful spot itself. On the good side, follow the same steps as for the painful side, but put south magnets on each of the points, one above, one below and one at the spot corresponding to the pain. This is a further elaboration of the left/right balancing principle.

For stubborn pain along the course of a meridian, we use the big shot technique. This technique takes advantage of the fact that the lo point of any meridian communicates with both the same meridian on the opposite side of the body and the meridian opposite it on the Chinese clock (see illustration). If the pain is an excess, to draw it away we tonify the lo of the meridian on the opposite side (because if one side is in excess the other is, relatively, deficient) and the lo of the opposite meridian on the Chinese clock, also on the opposite side. Then we disperse the two most painful spots on the reactive side.

The meridians opposite each other on the Chinese clock are:

Lung—Urinary Bladder	Large Intestine—Kidney
Stomach—Pericardium	Spleen—Triple Burner
Heart—Gall Bladder	Small Intestine—Liver

Chinese Clock

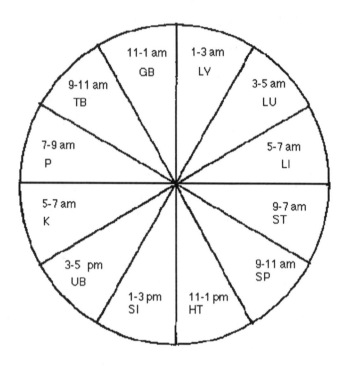

For example, excess pain on the right large intestine meridian would be treated by tonification of the large intestine lo on the left and tonification of the kidney lo on the left. Then sedate the two most painful spots on the large intestine on the right.

If the excess pain covers two or three meridian pathways use the group lo of the opposite polarity on the opposite extremity as the tonification point and the center of pain for sedation. The group lo for the arm Yin is P 5 (we use the point midway between the distral and prodmial finger joint on the pericardium meridian K8) for the arm Yang is TW 8 (we use TB 5 on the hand) for the leg Yin is SP 6 and for the leg Yang is GB 35.

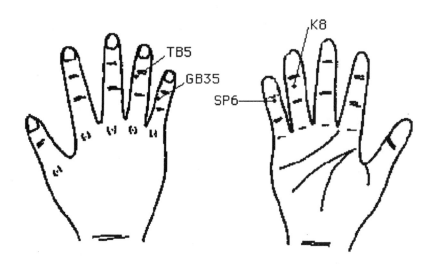

One very important treatment mentioned in Doctor Yoos' book involves the four pulse points. this treatment ensures proper circulation of blood to the head. If the head has a disturbance of blood flow and number of serious consequences can ensue.

Basically, the vertebral and carotid arteries supply blood to the head. We cannot palpate the vertibral artery, but it is connected to the radial artery via the subclavian artery so we can use L 9 on the radial artery as a diagnostic palpation point. We check the relative amounts of blood flowing in the carotid and radial artery to see if they are equal. If the carotid is thicker than the radial, we place a north magnet on C8 to sedate the excess and a south magnet on I2 to tonify the deficiency. If the radial pulse is thicker than the carotid, we place a south magnet on C8 and a north on I2. This therapy is valid in any case where the pulses are not in balance. I find it especially useful in cases of headache, dizziness, fuzzy headedness, emotional strain, fatigue, etc. Doctor Yoo suggests to use moxa needles or bloodletting if the pulse does not return to normal.

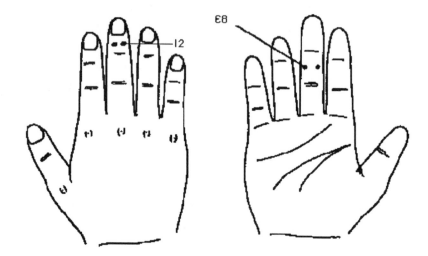

Another treatment that I use regularly and would like to mention here addresses the fire/water, adrenal exhaustion syndrome. It basically strengthens the adrenals and is very useful for palpitations, high blood pressure, flushed face with cold feet, stress, shoulder and neck tension, exhaustion, etc. The pulse is rapid but not floating and the abdominal diagnosis for this treatment is shown in the illustration.

If there is great sensitivity at the left K 27 and the right K 6 and their opposites are not sensitive, those two points alone should suffice. If all four points (left and right K 27 and K6) are sensitive, use them all. Use a north magnet on K 27 to bring the fire down, and a south on K 6 to bring the water up. In concert these two points balance the fire and water and produce remarkably good effects.

Adrenal Diagnsis

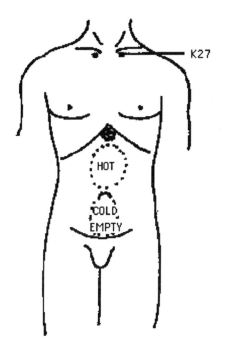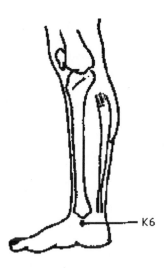

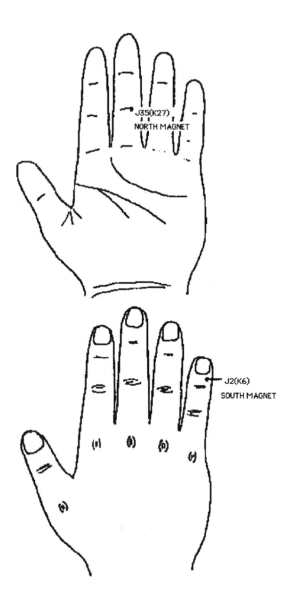

J35(K27)
NORTH MAGNET

J2(K6)
SOUTH MAGNET

Five Element and Constitutional Acupuncture

In chapters ten and eleven of his book, Doctor Tae-Woo Yoo explains his theories of the constitutional classification of people and the appropriate use of Five Element Theory acupuncture techniques for treatment of these constitutional types. In the clinic, I find the constitutional approach to diagnosis and treatment to be very accurate and effective.

Briefly, in this system, there are three basic constitutional types: Yang Excess, Yin Excess, and Kidney Excess. Each type tends to have a certain excess/deficient pattern in the relationships of the twelve Yin/Yang paired organs. These excess/deficient patterns can be determined by all of the traditional oriental diagnostic methods including pulse reading, taking medical history, abdominal palpation, back palpation, meridian pathway palpation, hand acupuncture point and meridian pathway palpation, tongue diagnosis, face diagnosis, etc. In some cases the patient may have a different constitution on each side of their body. These are called Compound types and can be somewhat complicated to diagnose and treat with the traditional methods.

After a brief review of the three constitutional types, I will explain a magnet diagnostic method that not only allows us to ascertain accurately the excess/deficient pattern, but also enables us to check to be sure that our treatment is the correct one to bring all the various disharmonies into balance. In other words, we can demonstrate finding the root imbalance. In some cases it may be more important first to deal with severe symptoms before the root, or to deal with these symptoms on some energetic level other than the Five Element Therapy, but it is still very important to know the root.

Yang Excess Constitution

Organs in excess: liver, heart, pericardium, large intestine, stomach, urinary bladder.

Organs in deficiency: gall bladder, small intestine, triple warmer, lung, spleen, kidney

The Yang Excess constitution usually has symptoms on the left side of the body, treatment is therefore applied to the left hand. If the person is Yang Excess but has symptoms on the right side of the body, the treatment is applied to the right hand. Excesses of the heart and liver are often seen in this constitution, although imbalances in any of the organ pairs are possible and encountered in clinic. Yang Excess constitution is usually quite responsive to treatment and improves rapidly. Encountered in this constitution are the full range of symptoms these disharmonies tend to produce, including spinal problems, impotence, gynecological problems, headaches (especially at the GV14 area), insomnia, tired eyes, arm, chest, and back neuralgias, gastrointestinal problems, nervousness, skin diseases, exhaustion, etc.

The following illustration shows the abdominal diagnostic points and points that are commonly sensitive on the hand and body meridians.

Yang Excess

EXCESS: Liver, Heart, Pericardium, Large Intestine, Stomach, Urinary Bladder
DEFICIENCY: Spleen, Lung, Kidney, Gall Bladder, Small Intemstine, Triple Warmer

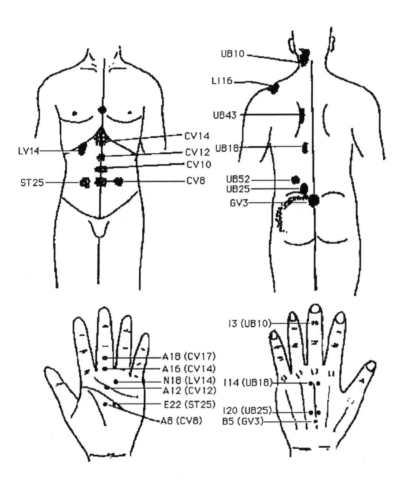

Yang Excess Points

Since sensitive spots indicate areas of congested energy, sensitive sopts on the limbs can be found on those meridians which are in excess in the Yang Excess Constitution. The mast commonly affected points are as follows:

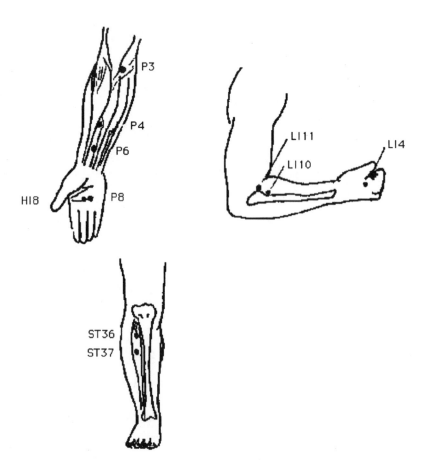

Kidney Excess Constitution

Organs in excess: kidney, liver, lung, small intestine, stomach, triple burner.

Organs in deficiency: urinary bladder, gall bladder, large intestine, heart, spleen, pericardium.

Kidney Excess constitution people are prone to develop problems on the right side of their bodies. Again, if the problem manifests itself on the left side of the body in a Kidney Excess constitution, the left hand is treated. Doctor Yoo explains that although in many schools of traditional oriental medical theory the Kidney is never in excess, in many cases this is not clinically true. Some Kidney Excess people form a lump near the triple warmer alarm point under the navel and in other places along the conception vessel. This lump is due to cold and deficiency in the Heart and Spleen and signifies an excess in the area (lower abdomen) controlled by the Kidneys. The lump must first be dispersed by sedating the Kidneys and Triple Warmer before the Kidney can be tonified. This symptom pattern tends to respond more slowly to treatment and chronic disorders can be difficult to cure. The symptoms in this constitution are the usual disharmonies encountered with such organ imbalances, including pain in the head and back of head, shoulder and other rheumatic pains, nasal problems, hemorrhoids and rectal problems, low blood pressure, allergies, urogenital problems, etc.

The following illustration shows the abdominal diagnostic points, back diagnostic points, and common meridian and hand sensitive points for the Kidney Excess Condition.

Kidney Excess Points

EXCESS: Kidney, Liver, Lung, Small Intestine, Stomach, Triple Warmer

DEFICIENT: Heart, Pericardium, Spleen, Urinary Bladder, Gall Bladder, Large Intestine

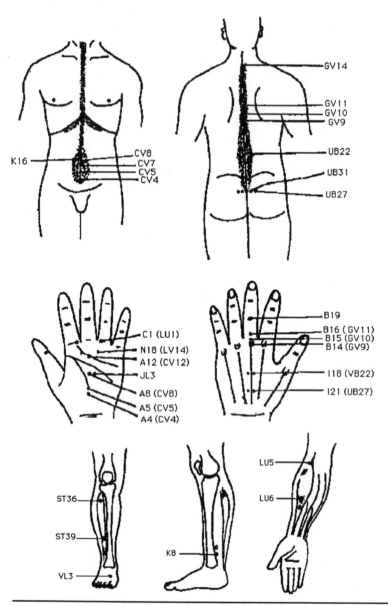

Yin Excess Constitution

Organs in excess: spleen lung heart pericardium gall
                         bladder urinary bladder
Organs in deficiency: stomach large intestine small intestine
                         triple warmer liver kidney
                         The large intestine can be either excess
                         or deficient in this symptom pattern.

The Yin Excess symptom pattern tends to produce overweight
people who eat and sleep too much. They are often the most
difficult to diagnose by traditional methods, but readily respond
to the correct therapy. Their symptoms include expected
imbalances such as aenemia, neuralgias, high blood pressure,
arthritis, corpulence, gallstones, pancreatitis, low energy,
paralysis, convulsions, asthma, diabetes, bone problems, etc.

Yin Excess Points

EXCESS: Spleen, Lung, Heart, Pericardium, Gall Bladder, Urinary Bladder (sometimes Large Intestine)

DEFICIENT: Liver, Kidneys, Stomach, Large Intestine, Small Intestine, Triple Burner.

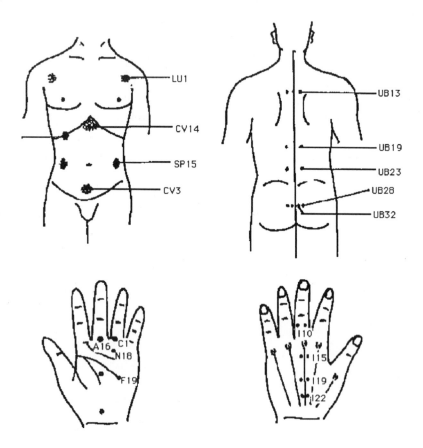

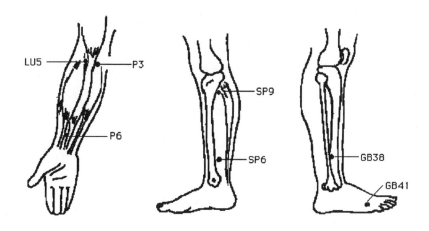

It must be remembered that a constitutional diagnosis should not be made by symptomology alone and that all available diagnostic tools and approaches should be used. Many, if not most symptoms can occur in each of the three constitutions. When diagnosing with magnets, it is important to check both hands to determine if the patient is a Compound type. Clinical experience will show that often the obvious is merely a superficial view of the whole picture.

Therapy

Generally, in treating patients, the right hand is used for treating diseases that manifest on the right side of the body, and the left hand is used for treating diseases manifest on the left side of the body. Usually the two ulnar or lateral fingers (hands outstretched at chest level with palms facing away from the body) are used for therapy, although both hands can be used in especially difficult or chronic cases. For example, if a disease is manifest on the right side of the body, the ulnar side fingers of the right hand are used in therapy. If this is unsuccessful, the radial fingers of the left hand can be used, as these fingers correspond to the right side of the body. If a patient is a Yang Excess constitution, but shows no physical sign of disease on either side of the body, treat the right hand. Yin Excess can be treated right for female, left for male; or right for a Yin disease and left for a Yang disease; or right for right handed and left for left handed people.

Treatments for the Three Constitutions

The magnet diagnosis to be presented later in this chapter is the method I use to clearly show which side has the most therapeutic value for all of the patients' disharmonies. In treating the Compound constitutional types, we ascertain the constitution of each side of the body and treat accordingly. The Kidney Excess constitution has its diagnostic sensitive points on the midline so the other constitution is found and treated on its side with the Kidney Excess automatically treated on the opposite side. With magnet diagnosis it is quite easy to define clearly which side to treat even with Compound types.

Doctor Yoos' book presents four techniques for applying Five Element Theory to the treatment of the Three Constitutions. The basic theories are: for deficiency use tonification, for excess use sedation, for cold symptoms tonify and remove cold, and for heat symptoms sedate and remove heat. The cold and heat removing therapies are used for severe deficiency/excess symptoms. In severe deficiency with a pulse rate of seventy beats per minute or below, the cold removing therapy is used. In cases of severe excess with a pulse rate of eighty beats per minute or more, the heat removing therapy is used. In less drastic circumstances the usual tonification and sedation approaches are utilized.

The tonification and sedation therapies employ the classical nurturing and control cycle relationships to achieve their ends. This includes the tonification of the mother, sedation of the son, and either sedating or tonifying othe controlling organ by the control cycle. Generally, the control cycle is treated first.

To tonify any organ, determine which element it belongs to and whether it is a Yin or Yang organ. If the organ is Yin, our therapy will remain in the Yin organs. If the organ is Yang , our therapy will be directed at the Yang organs. Since we are tonifying the organ in question, we must first reduce the effect of the controlling organ via the control cycle. This is accomplished by sedating (using a north side magnet) both the horary point of the controlling organ (the horary point is the Five Element point on the meridian in question that is of the same element as the meridian itself—the fire point of a fire meridian, for example) and the point on the target meridian that is the same element of the controlling meridian. Next we have to tonify the horary point of the mother meridian via the nurturing cycle and the point on the target meridian that is the same element as the mother meridian. Tonification is accomplished with a south side magnet. For example, to tonify the spleen, we sedate the wood point of the liver and the wood point of the spleen and we tonify the fire point of the heart and the fire point of the spleen.

To sedate any organ, we want to increase the effect of the controlling organ, so the first technique is to tonify the horary point of the controlling meridian and the point on the target meridian that is the same element as the controlling meridian. Next we sedate the horary point of the son meridian and sedate the point on the target meridian that is the same element as the son meridian via the nurturing cycle.

For example, to sedate the stomach, we first tonify the wood point of the gall bladder and the wood point of the stomach and then sedate the metal point of the large intestine and the metal point of the stomach.

To tonify and remove cold, treatment is used in cases of severe deficiency. The treatment not only removes cold, but also adds heat. In this treatment, the horary (water) point of the water Yin or Yang meridian is sedated and the water point of the meridian in question is sedated. If the problem meridian is one of the water meridians, (Kidney or Urinary Bladder), the horary point is used and the wood point of the corresponding son meridian is sedated. The horary point of any meridian broadcasts its element correspondances to its same element point on each of the other meridians. The climate that corresponds to water is cold. By sedating the horary point of the water meridian and the water point of the meridian in question, the original energetic source and the local manifestations of cold are sedated. In the case of the water meridians themselves, wood is the son of water via the nurturing cycle. We sedate the son. The wood (son) meridian is the point most expedient for draining cold from the water meridians.

The second part of our therapy involves adding heat to the meridian in question. The same logic applies—we must tonify the horary point of the fire meridians because hot is the climate associated with fire. For this purpose the heart is used for all of the Yin meridians, except the pericardium which uses its own horary point. The small intestine fire point is used for all of theYang meridians, except the triple burner which uses its own horary point. We also tonify the fire point of the meridian in question. In case the meridian in question is itself a fire meridian, the horary point is used and the mother meridian's horary point is used. Because wood is the mother of fire in the nurturing cycle, the wood point of the Yin or Yang wood meridian is used.

For example, cold therapy for the spleen entails sedating the water points of the kidney and spleen, and tonifying the fire points of the heart and spleen. If the triple burner is involved, we sedate the water points of the urinary bladder and triple burner and tonify the fire points of the triple burner and gall bladder (because wood is the mother of fire).

The Sedation and Removal of Heat or Inflammation Therapy is used in cases of severe excess. The logic follows the same line as above, but the treatment principle is opposite. In this case, the water horary point is tonified and the water point of the meridian is tonified. In the case of the water meridians themselves, the horary point is used with the tonification of the metal point on the metal meridian (metal is the mother of water). Now the the fire horary points are sedated on the fire meridians themselves as are the fire points of the Yin or Yang meridian. In the case of the fire meridians themselves, the horary points are sedated and the earth point of the earth (son) meridian following in the nurturing cycle is sedated. For all the Yin organs the fire point of the heart meridian is used, except for the pericardium which uses its own fire point. The fire point of the small intestine is used for all of the Yang meridians except for the triple burner which uses its own fire point.

For instance, if the large intestine is in severe excess, we tonify the water points of the urinary bladder and large intestine. Then we sedate the fire points of the small intestine and large intestine.

If we had excess fire in the pericardium, we would tonify the water point of the kidneys and the water point of the pericardium. Then we would sedate the fire point of the pericardium and the earth point of the spleen (earth is the son of fire).

These treatment methods produce good results in the clinic and can all be done with magnets and hand acupuncture points. In all the points calling for tonification use a magnet with its south side on the skin, and in all the points calling for sedation use a magnet with its north side touching the skin. Always check the pulse, diagnostic palpation areas, and muscle test before and after the magnets are in place. After the magnets are in place, the pulse should change for the better, the diagnostic areas should be less sensitive, and the muscle test should show an increase in strength. A fifteen to twenty minute treatment usually works well with this method, but tailor your therapy to each individual case.

Magnet Diagnosis

Magnet diagnosis of the three constitutions or any organ/ meridian imbalance is both simple and accurate. We know that the energy of a magnetic field travels from north to south and that this energy will affect the bioelectric energy traveling in the meridians, especially in the hand meridians. We also know that the meridians of the hand directly affect corresponding organs and body terrain. The places where magnetic energy will most efficiently affect hand acupuncture meridian energy are at the middle and distal joints of the fingers. Here is where the first tool (bar magnet) that I mentioned in the chapter on magnets comes into play. The length of the tool and spacing of the magnets allows it to influence the hand acupuncture meridians efficently.

To diagnose the relative excess or deficient condition of any meridian, simply place the bar magnet between the middle and distal joints of the finger on the course of the meridian in question and perform one of the muscle tests (explained in the chapter on muscle testing). Then reverse the polarity of the bar magnet and repeat the procedure. If a meridian is in a state of deficiency, placing the magnetic flow against the flow of the meridian will weaken it even further, throwing it more out of balance and producing a weak muscle test. In other words, sedating a weak meridian weakens the whole energy system of a patient and tonifying a weak meridian system strengthens the whole energy system of the patient. This shows clearly with the muscle test.

Deficient meridians:

——————>North——South——————————>Strong muscle test
——————>South—North——————————>Weak muscle test

If a meridian is in excess, putting a magnetic flow against the flow of the meridian (sedating) will produce a strong muscle test. If the magnetic flow is placed with the flow of the meridian (tonifying) we drive the meridian further out of balance thus producing weaker muscle test.

Excess Meridians

——————>North——South——————————>Weak muscle test
——————>South—North——————————>Strong muscle test

If a meridian is almost in balance, the bar magnet will not cause a great variation in the muscle test in either direction.

It is a simple matter to tape the bar magnet to each of the hand meridians and do one of the muscle tests. This will give us the relative excess or deficient state of all the meridians. The results can be confirmed by any of the conventional diagnostic approaches. This will leave us with a clear constitutional portrait of the patient.

As Doctor Yoo states in his book, "The principal difficulty, and the reason that Five Element Therapy is an advanced technique, is that it depends on an accurate diagnosis of excess, deficiency, cold, and heat and which organs have these imbalances. This is a subject that requires much study and experience to master." (Yoo, p.314)

In his book, Doctor Yoo describes various conventional diagnostic methods and mentions some of the most common disharmony scenarios for each of the three constitutions. Another method of finding the root imbalance employs the use of the bar magnet. Because of its effect on the meridian energy, the bar magnet can be used as a treatment device as well as a diagnostic tool.

When your diagnosis is complete, including all signs, symptoms, and excess/deficiency information from the bar magnet diagnosis, choose the most likely root cause of all the other imbalances and treat that meridian with the bar magnet . If you choose a meridian in excess, tape the bar magnet on its course in the sedation mode (south magnet facing the energetic beginning of the meridian and north facing the energetic end of the meridian). This will treat that meridian. If you choose a meridian in deficiency, tape the bar magnet on its course in the tonification mode (north magnet facing the energetic beginning of the meridian and south facing the energetic end of the meridian). This will treat that meridian.

Then, with another bar magnet, go back and test all the meridians again. If all the meridians have returned to balance, you have found the root cause of all the imbalances in the system. If after this second test all the meridians are not in balance, we must choose another meridian to treat with the bar magnet and do the second test again. When we do find the meridian that when treated balances all the others, we treat that meridian with the appropriate Five Element Therapy.

With practice and experience this method is not as time consuming as it may appear. In most cases there will be no need to test all the meridians. By testing just a few we can ascertain the constitution and from there calculate the most likely scenario of disharmony. For instance, only in the Yin Excess Constitution are the spleen, lung, and gall bladder all in excess.

Only in the Yang Excess Constitution are the stomach and large intestine in excess. And only the Kidney Excess Contitution has heart, pericardium, and liver all in excess. The Kidney Excess Constitiution is the only one in which the Kidney is in excess. In practice, hoever, the Kidney is sometimes deficient in this constitiution which indicates a less advanced stage of disharmony.

In the clinic, the constitutional view of patients holds remarkably valid. In some cases, no meridians are out of balance, which will show in the muscle test as no big difference between when the bar magnet is in the tonification mode and the sedation mode. In other cases, the imbalances will not follow the exact pattern described, although in my experience this is much less often than I would have guessed. In any case, the bar magnet method is one very precise diagnostic method of ascertaining the energetic state of the patient. It is truly satisfying to find a diagnostic method that can show the disharmony and potential result of the treatment before therapy is applied.

The Five Element Points in hand acupuncture are arranged in a pattern that is quite simple and easy to grasp. It is so easy, in fact, that one does not have to know the hand meridian system in great detail in order to utilize this advanced treatment technique. The accompanying illustration clearly shows the pattern for both Yin and Yang channels.

Five Element Therapy can be accompainied with both local and three burner therapy, as explained in the chapter on local treatments.

Five Element Points - Yang Channels

channel → element ↓	TB	SI	LI	GB	UB	ST
+ Metal	L1	H1	D1	M32	I39	E45
# Water	L2	H2	D2	M31	I38	E44
@ Wood	L5	H5	D5	M28	I35	E40
~ Fire	L6	H6	D6	M27	I34	E39
* Earth	L7	H7	D7	M26	I33	E38

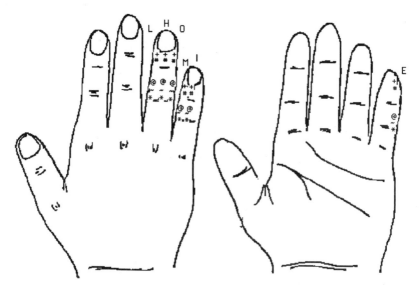

Sedation Technique: Tonify Controller, Sedate the Son
Tonification Technique: Sedate the Controller, Tonify the Mother

Five Element Points - Yin Channels

channel → element ↓	LU	P	HT	LV	SP	K
+ Metal	C7	K8	G9	N7	F7	J5
# Water	C5	K6	G7	N9	F9	J7
@ Wood	C13	K15	G15	N1	F1	J1
~ Fire	C11	K13	G13	N3	F3	J2
* Earth	C9	K10	G11	N5	F5	J3

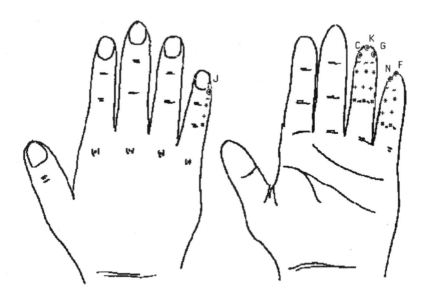

The Five Element Cycles

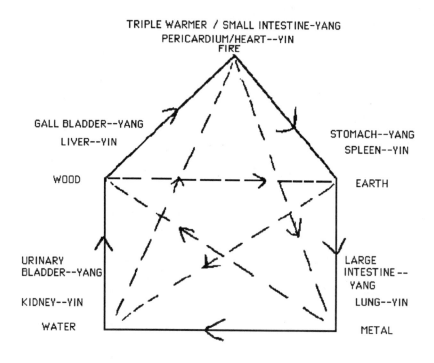

Eight Extraordinary Vessels

In the words of Penn Chiao, "Only those who master the Eight Extra Vessels besides the twelve major meridians can make a diagnosis and only those who know how to use the Extra Vessels can eradicate the illness, which is often deeper than one thinks." (Jeynes, p.1)

Volumes have been written on the Eight Extraordinary Vessels or Extra Meridians. It is not my purpose to review the subject entirely, but rather to present simple, effective techniques for diagnosis and treatment of these very important energy systems.

The Traditional Method

One method of diagnosis is to use symptom/sign complexes of the vessels and their pathways. With that in mind, the following illustrations give a general symptomology and pathway guide. Because of the Yin/Yang-north/south nature of magnet treatment, I always use the master and coupled points of the vessel pairs. If you have chosen the vessels by this method, you simply place a south magnet on one of the two points and a north on the other and muscle test. Then reverse the north south arrangement and test again. Use the arrangement.that tests the strongest.

Treatment Points for the Eight Extra Meridians

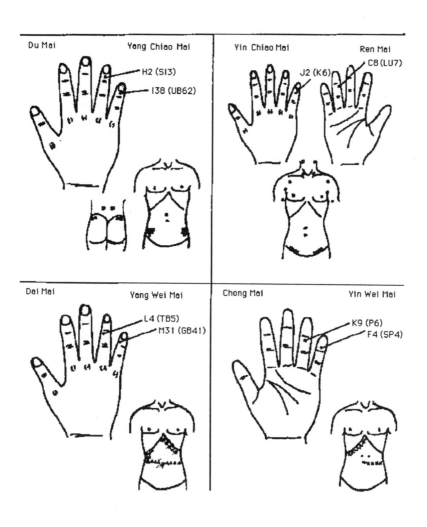

Du Mai
Yang Chiao Mai
H2 (SI3)
I38 (UB62)

Yin Chiao Mai
Ren Mai
J2 (K6)
C8 (LU7)

Dai Mai
Yang Wei Mai
L4 (TB5)
M31 (GB41)

Chong Mai
Yin Wei Mai
K9 (P6)
F4 (SP4)

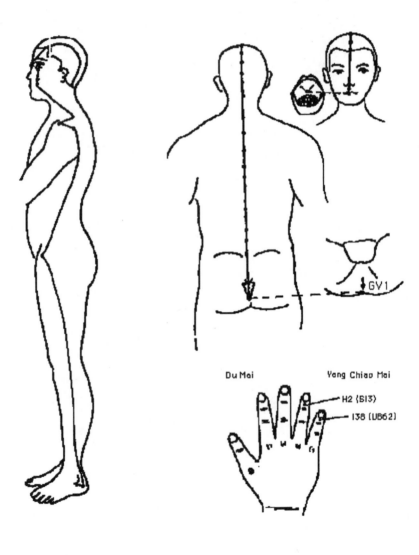

Du Mai — Yang Chiao Mai

H2 (SI3)

I38 (UB62)

Ren Mai and Yin Qiao Mai

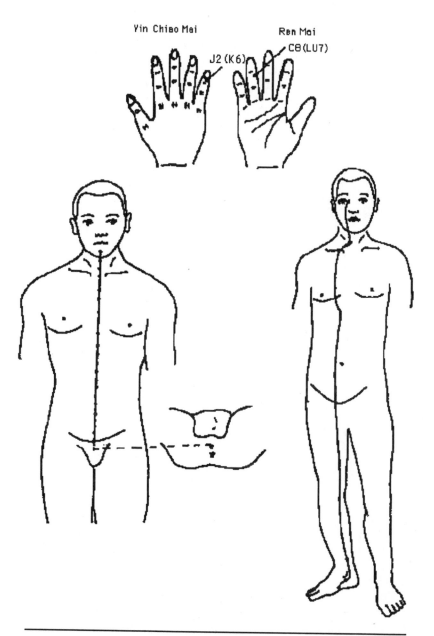

Dai Mai and Yang Wei Mai

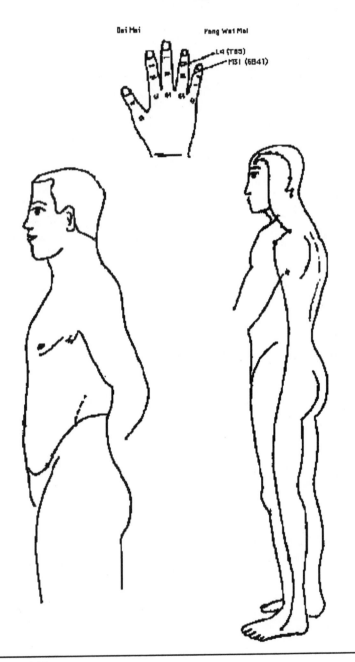

Chong Mai and Yin Wei Mai

Chong Mai   Yin Wei Mai

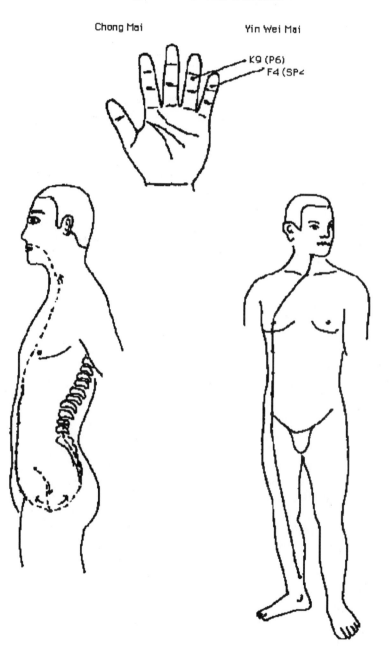

K9 (P6)
F4 (SP<

Ms. Tokito's Method

On page 150 of *Extraordinary Vessels,* Kiiko Matsumoto and
Steven Birch, present the work of Ms. Tokito. Briefly, Ms.
Tokito believes that "all disease results from an imbalance
between the triple warmer and pericardium, master of the
heart, ming men." It is here that "the transformations that
produce each of the specific energies take place." Ms. Tokito
relies on the pulse for her diagnosis and presenting symptoms
are not utilized for her treatment plan. The idea is that by
balancing the deeper energies all other imbalances will be
corrected from within. Using the Eight Extraordinary Vessels
to access these deeper energies,her diagnosis leads to treatment
by one of three groups of extra vessel points. Each group
contains four points thus utilizing the master and coupled
points of two pairs of extra vessels. Her therapy is accomplished by inserting two copper and two zinc needles in a prear-
ranged pattern into the points. Signs of effectiveness of the
treatment can be readily observed in the evening of the pulses
and the relaxation of the neck muscles. The needles remain for
ten to twenty minutes and are removed in a specific order/
pattern also. The key point in this method is correct diagnosis
by pulse. The therapy is standardized after the diagnosis.

I have used this method extensively in my practice and have
ben very pleased with the results. The therapy seems to re-
charge the inner energetic batteries—if fatique is one of the
patient's main symptoms, I immediately consider this approach.
When I began using this method, I was lucky enough to have
several patients whose pulses were easy to read. After obtain-
ing good results from this method, I began to consider alternate
methods of diagnosis, because Ms. Tokito warns us not to use
her method if the pulse is not clear. I came up with a magnet
diagnostic method on body acupuncture points and eventually
assimilated that method into both diagnosis and treatment in
my work with hand acupuncture, with continued good results.

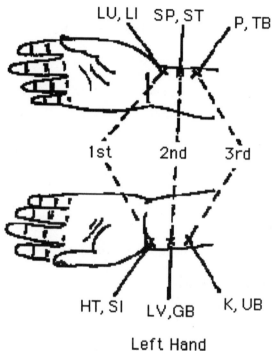

Right Hand

LU, LI   SP, ST   P, TB

1st   2nd   3rd

HT, SI   LV, GB   K, UB

Left Hand

The three possible point combinations for this therapy are:

Weak Ming Men left third position deep pulse is stronger than the right third position deep pulse

1 Left Pericardium 6	Yin wei mo	south magnet copper needle
2 Right Urinary Bladder 62	Yang chiao Mo	north magnet zinc needle
3 Left Spleen 4	Chong Mo	north magnet zinc needle
4 Right Small Intestine 3	Du Mo	south magnet copper needle

Weak Triple Warmer right third position deep pulse is stronger than the left third position deep pulse and in the 2nd position the Gall Bladder is stronger than the Stomach at the superfical level.

1 Right Triple Burner 5	Yang Wei Mo	south magnet copper needle
2 Left Kidney 6	Yin chiao Mo	north magnet zinc needle
3 Right Gall Bladder 41	Dai Mo	north magnet zinc needle
4 Left Lung 7	Ren Mo	south magnet copper needle

Weak Triple Warmer right third position deep pulse is stronger than the left third position deep pulse and in the secondsuperficial position the Stomach is stronger than the Gall Bladder.

1. Left Triple Warmer 5	Yang Wei Mo	south magnet copper needle
2 Right Kidney 6	Yin Chiao Mo	north magnet zinc needle
3 Left Gall Bladder 41	Dai Mo	north magnet zinc needle
4 Right lung 7	Ren Mo	south magnet copper needle

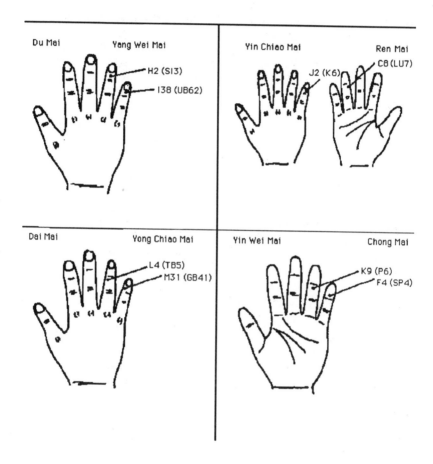

Du Mai   Yang Wei Mai

H2 (SI3)
I38 (UB62)

Yin Chiao Mai   Ren Mai

J2 (K6)
C8 (LU7)

Dai Mai   Yong Chiao Mai

L4 (TB5)
M31 (GB41)

Yin Wei Mai   Chong Mai

K9 (P6)
F4 (SP4)

With Ms Tokito's method the points are treated in the order given. The first and fourth points are needled with copper (tonic) needles or south magnets and the second and third points are needled with zinc (sedative) needles or north magnets. The first two points are treated and the practitioner waits for the pulse to become more balanced and the neck muscles to relax. This usually happens within a few minutes. Then the remaining needles or magnets are applied.

Diagnosis with magnets alone is possible, but I usually try to read the pulse and do a magnet diagnosis to confirm my findings. To diagnose with magnets, simply apply the first two magnets of each of the three groups(one group at a time) and muscle test. The group with the strongest muscle test reaction is the one to use in your therapy.

For example, first apply a south magnet to left pericardium 6 and a north magnet to right urinary bladder 62 Wait a few seconds and muscle test. Remove the magnets. Then apply a south on the left triple warmer 5 and a north on the right kidney 6. Wait a few seconds, test, and remove the magnets. Next, place a south on the right triple warmer 5 and a north on the left kidney 6 and again test and remove the magnets. If the first pair tested showed the strongest response that is the symptom pattern to treat. Our treatment would be to tape a south magnet on the left pericardium and a north magnet to the right urinary bladder 62, wait a few seconds and check the pulse and neck muscles to assure a positive change and then apply the remaining north on the left spleen 4 and a south on the right small intestine 3.

Allow the magnets to remain in place for ten to twenty minutes or until the patient becomes agitated. The other symptom patterns are also treated in the same order presented and the magnets are removed in exactly the reverse order that they were applied.

Dr. Manaka's Method

In 1985, Doctor Yoshi Manaka held a seminar in San Francisco to teach, among other things, a method of diagnosis and treatment of the extra vessels. The diagnosis used abdominal palpation and the treatment was performed using ion cords. This diagnostic technique involved palpating the abdomen at specific areas to ascertain the relative tightness, pain, or softness of the tissues. In diseased tissue, pathological changes take place due to oxygen deprivation. These changes can manifest as pain, or spasms of varying degrees (from a slight tightness to a hard lump, flacidity, or pulsing). Such changes can indicate pathology in the tissue itself or the tissue can reflect deeper problems.

When using abdominal palpation as a means of diagnosis, if the correct treatment is discovered and applied, the reflex areas of pain,spasms, pulsing, etc. will change for the better in a matter of minutes. If no change appears, the choice of treatment is incorrect. When a change does appear, it signifies a greater flow of life force and oxygen-bearing blood to whatever area precipitated the reflex area. This of course promotes healing. An Ion pumps is a highly conductive cord with a diode inserted along its length. The diode allows certain ions to flow in only one direction along the length of the wire that is the pump. This results in a system where one area is receiving these ions or being tonified with them and the opposite area is loosing these ions or being sedated. In other words, a strong Yin/Yang polarity is developed, just as in the application of a north and south magnet therapy.

This seminar changed the way I practiced acupuncture. Ion cords were the most potent tools of my trade until I began to apply magnets to hand acupuncture. In using the extraordinary vessels with this diagnostic method, the master and coupled points of the vessels are used on the same side of the body. In most cases, the side of the body with the problem is the one to use. If there is a question about which side of the body to use, you can apply the treatment to each side separately and see which gives the stronger muscle test and greatest release of the reflex areas and other present symptoms. Often you will diagnose two or three abdominal symptom patterns, and in these cases it works well to choose the most prominent reflex area as the main treatment and the second most prominent as the secondary treatment.

Abdominal Diagnosis for Eight Extra Meridians

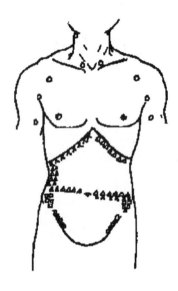

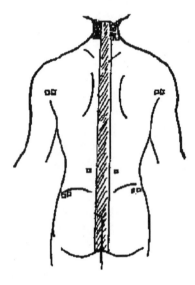

Symbols indicate spasm
pressure/pain reaction

□ = Du Mai (SI3)
    Yang Qiao Mai (UB62)

O = Ren Mai (LU7)
    Yin Qiao Hai (K6)

x = Chong Mai (SP4)
    Yin Wei Mai (P6)

△ = Dai Mai (GB41)
    Yang Wei Mai (TB5)

Treatment Points for Eight Extra Meriaians

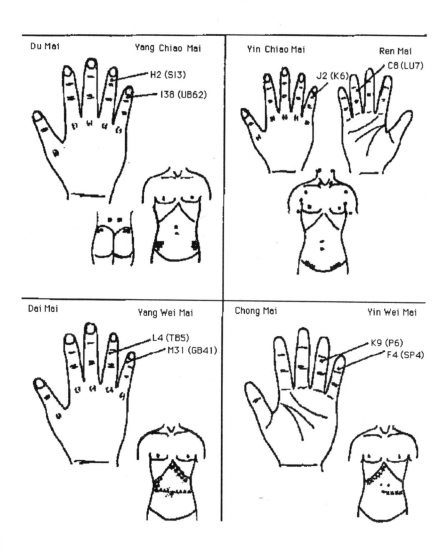

Du Mai   Yang Chiao Mai

H2 (SI3)

138 (UB62)

Yin Chiao Mai   Ren Mai

C8 (LU7)

J2 (K6)

Dai Mai   Yang Wei Mai

L4 (TB5)

M31 (GB41)

Chong Mai   Yin Wei Mai

K9 (P6)

F4 (SP4)

You can test for all possible combinations, but usually the primary treatment is applied to the most reactive side and the secondary treatment is applied to the other side. Refrain from using other points during this treatment, as side effects can occur. You are treating powerful energies at a deep level and "more is not always better." In the accompanying illustrations you will be shown the abdominal symptom patterns for the pairs of extra vessels used in this method as well as the reactive painful areas along the meridians. The usual north south arrangement of magnets will be noted, but never guess at the polarity, always muscle test to be sure you are strengthening the system. Also, always check to be sure that the reactive symptom pattern becomes less reactive.

There are two special treatments that Steven Birch presented in one of his seminars on Doctor Manakas' work. These are not extraordinary vessel treatments per se, but do lend themselves well to magnet treatment.

The first, "Tai Ji Treatment," stimulates all 12 major meridians and aligns them in their proper Yin/Yang polarity through the meeting points of the three Yin of the arm, the three Yang of the arm, the three Yin of the leg, and the three Yang of the leg.

Pressure pain at two of the three following points is a good diagnostic guideline for the use of this treatment: K 16, LV 13, and SP 15. It is useful for stress, extreme fatigue, knee joint pain , whiplash problems (especially with front to back movement problems), nervousness, and mental problems. Miki Shima of the topograghical school of acupuncture recommends this treatment for all menstrual problems. The treatment is the bilateral use of the following four pairs of hand points. SP 6 south, P 5—we use P4— north, TW 8—we use TB 5 south, GB 35 or north.

Tai Ji Treatment

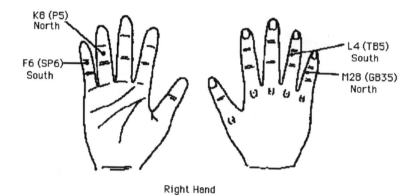

Right Hand

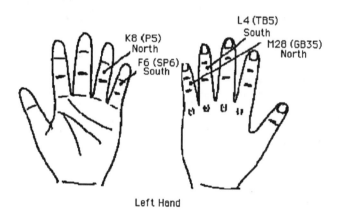

Left Hand

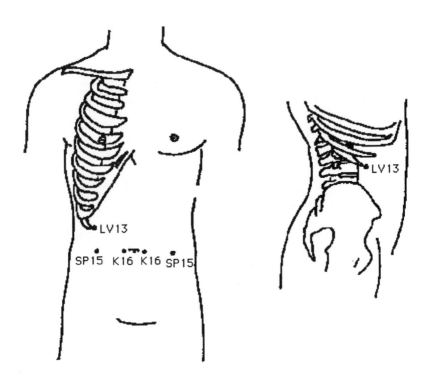

Another specific whiplash and any spinal problem treatment is SI 3 north, UB 62 south, GB 41 north, and TW 5 south. These points can be used bilaterally, on one side alone, or one pair on each side. This treatment is especially good for problems of rotation. Remember to always use the eight extra vessels in their traditional paired relationships for these treatments.

The Infinity Method

In 1987, I attended a seminar by Kiiko Matsumoto concentrating on another technique of abdominal diagnosis for extra vessel therapy. Much of this seminar was the presentation of Doctor Kawai's work in this field—Infinity Treatments.

This method is somewhat simpler than the Manaka method as the polarity of the treatment is set exactly by the abdominal findings. Each symptom pattern uses two sets of master/coupled points although in some instances one set may be omitted according to symptoms present. Doctor Kawai has added to the traditional list of extraordinary vessels through a theory beyond the scope of this work. The practical result is a couple of non-traditional points used in the therapy which will be presented later. There are four basic magnet patterns in this method of therapy diagnosed by abdominal palpation and presenting symptoms. The following illustrations will show the abdominal symptom patterns, symptomatology, and magnet polarity arrangements for these therapies.

Infinity Treatment: Liver Pattern

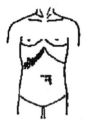

SYMPTOMATOLOGY: LV disorders, (hepatitis, right side chest distress, PMS, LV headaches, LV defieciency, backaches, muscle spasms, especially along the spine.

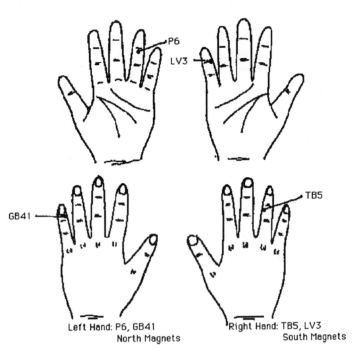

Left Hand: P6, GB41
North Magnets

Right Hand: TB5, LV3
South Magnets

Infinity Treatment: Chong and Yin Wei
Dai and Yang Wei - Heart Pattern

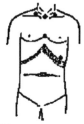

Diagnostic Reflex Points:

SYMPTOMATOLOGY: Heart pain, tightness and full fullness in the chest, palpitations with anxiety, congestive heart failure, high blood pressure, anemia, gynerological disorders, male sexual irregularities, digestive disorders in general, abdominal pain or colic, pain after meals, belching, food retension, abdomial rumblings, anorexia, vomitting, arthritic conditions, muscular disturbances, acute lumbar pain, sciatica

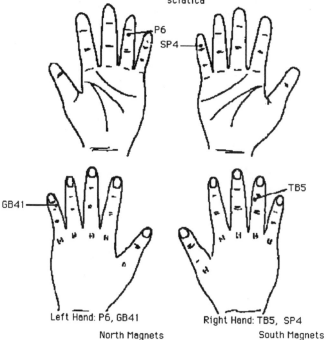

Left Hand: P6, GB41   Right Hand: TB5, SP4
  North Magnets   South Magnets

Infinity treatment: Stomach Pattern

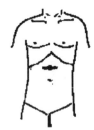

SYMPTOMATOLOGY:gastritis, irritable stomach from stress, heart burn, nausea, ulcer, stomach flu, any stomach disorder.

Diagnostic Reflex Points:

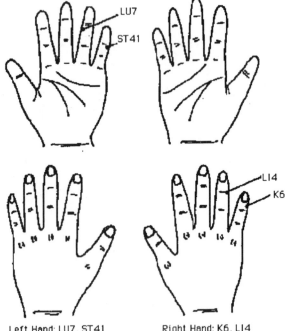

Left Hand: LU7, ST41
North Magnets

Right Hand: K6, LI4
South Magnets

Infinity Treatment: Ren and Yin Qiao
Du and Yang Qiao

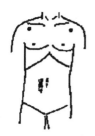

SYMPTOMATOLOGY: Cardiac asthma, bronchial asthma, asthma with allergies, diabetes, kidney disorders (nephritis, nephrosis,...) kidney deficient backache, enuiesis, difficulty hearing, impotence, prostatitis, irregular menstuation, dysmenorrhea, infertility, PMS, cold feet, cold back poor circulation, constipation, hemorrhoids, colic, fullness or heavy sensation in the head, vertigo, stiffness and pain along the spinal column, herniated disc, rheumatic conditions, upper limb problems associated with the SI meridian, shoulder pain bursitis.

Diagnostic Reflex Points:
LU1, ST25, 26, 27 LU7, UB13, K6, CV9, CV7

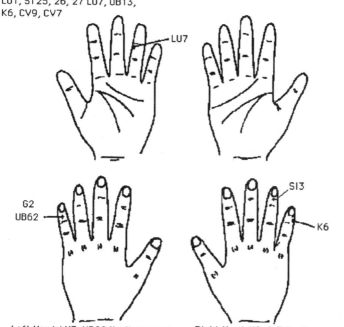

Left Hand: LU7, UB62 North magnets   Right Hand: K6, SI3 South magnets

There are two special treatments associated with the heart pattern that prove very effective and should be mentioned. For knee pain—use TW 5 south , GB 41 north, P 6 north, and spleen 4 south,all on the painful side. For shoulder pain associated with the triple warmer meridian, use TW 5 south and SP 4 north on the painful side and GB 41 north and P 6 south on the other side.

Shoulder Treatment

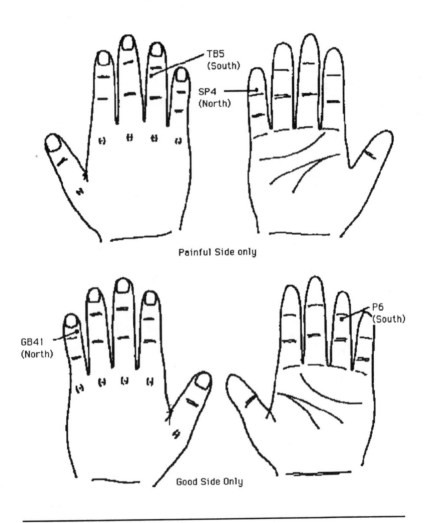

Painful Side only

Good Side Only

Knee Treatment

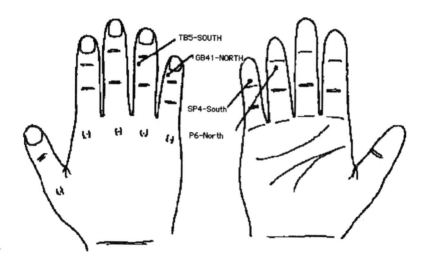

TB5-SOUTH

GB41-NORTH

SP4-South

P6-North

All points used on painful side

There are two other abdominal diagnostic methods I would like to present here. Both of them were gleaned from lectures by Mikki Shima on various aspects of polarity acupuncture. Both are useful in clinic. The testing method is to have the patient place his thumb and forefinger at the place indicated on the chart and to O-ring test the other hand. The treatment is directed at the pair of channels and side of the body showing the greatest weakness.

O-Ring Test

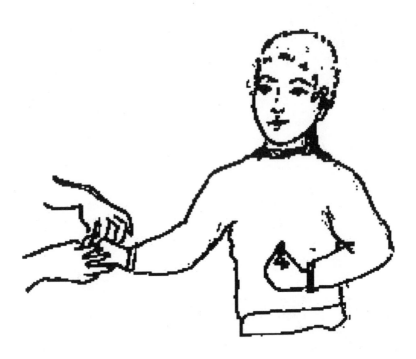

Traditional Extra Meriaians

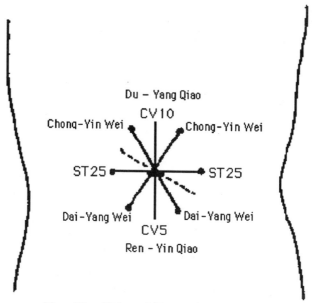

Du – Yang Qiao
CV10
Chong–Yin Wei · · Chong–Yin Wei
ST25 · · ST25
Dai–Yang Wei · Dai–Yang Wei
CV5
Ren – Yin Qiao

Non Traditional Extra Meriaians

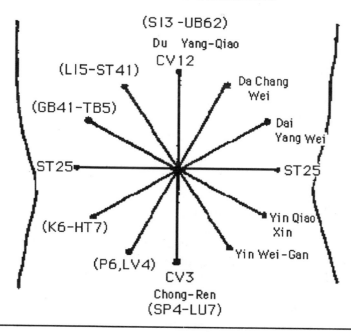

(SI3 –UB62)
Du   Yang–Qiao
CV12
(LI5–ST41)
Da Chang Wei
(GB41–TB5)
Dai Yang Wei
ST25 · · ST25
(K6–HT7)
Yin Qiao Xin
(P6,LV4)
Yin Wei –Gan
CV3
Chong–Ren
(SP4–LU7)

Divergent Meridians

Divergent meridian therapy is one of the least publicized areas of Chinese Medicine. There are several diagnostic and treatment methods that lend themselves well to magnet therapy with hand acupuncture. In diagnosing the divergents we must remember that they have more than one function so certain diagnostic methods may be specific for or at least relate more to one function than another.

To review, several of the specific functions of the divergents are: to bring Yin to the head, to link the Yin and Yang paired organs together at a deep level, to bring vital energy to smaller channels not reached by the main meridians, and to bring wei chi to the depths of the body to protect the organs.

The divergent meridians are Yin/Yang paired just like the major meridians, and most have an upper and lower meeting point or zone. Various sources give different locations for some of the meeting points, so it is interesting to note that the classics speak of zones, too.

The common meeting points are:

Divergent Pair Upper Meeting Lower Meeting

Divergent Pair	Upper Meeting	Lower Meeting
UB/KI	UB 10,11	UB40 (54)
GB/LIV	GB 1	GB 30
ST/SP	ST 1 UB 1	ST 30
HT/SI	UB 1	HE 1
TB/PER	TB 16	GB12
LI/LU	SI 17	ST 12

Divergent therapy always uses one or more of these points.

In the Su Wen there are three statements concerning the divergent channels: the perverse chi is flowing in the opposite direction as the chi in the main channel; the symptoms are intermittent and one sided; and therapy is to puncture the opposite side.

Generally diagnosis of this problem of perverse chi in the channels involves having the conditions of intermittent pain, one sided pain, no obvious cause from the environment, and the involvement of the organ of which ever divergent is affected (there will be some symptoms of the organ when the pain is apparent).

The treatment is to tonify the well or extremity end point on the non-painfull side to bring wei or defensive energy chi to the divergent meridian and to tonify GV 20, through which all divergents pass as they relate to their opposite side. This prevents the pain from changing sides. Finally, sedate the two (or one in some cases) meeting zones of the channel involved on the painful side.

Another method of diagnosing and treating the divergents is to determine which channel is out of balance based upon symptomology, regions of pathology, and abdominal diagnostic points as follows:

UB/KI=Cv3, KI 16, KI and UB disease, anus and urinary tract disease, Gyn, lumbago, nasal congestion, and symptoms of Dai Mo symptom pattern

GB/LIV GB 24, LIV 14, GB and LIV disease, muscle and tendon problems, neurosis, coldness, numbness, rheumatic bone diseases, genital itching, priapism

ST/SP CV 12, LIV 13, St and Sp diseases, muscle pains pertaining' to stomach spleen pathology

SI/HE CV4, CV 14, Heart and Small Intestine diseases, neurosis disease, urinary tract problems with hematuria.

TB/PER CV5, CV 17, circulatory problems, cardialgia, hypertension, numbness, edema, TB area arm pain, side effects of divergent meridian treatment and to prevent same.

LI/LU ST 27, LU1, Lung and Large intestine organ problems, diarrhea, asthma bronchitis, hemorrhoids.

Choose the channel with the most Yang (pain/sensitivity) symptoms for this method. Two points will be used for therapy, one from the upper meeting points, and either the source, lo or ho (promixal five element point) of the chosen channel. Generally, the divergent channels flow from the inferior to the superior part of the body but always muscle test to be sure your north south alignment is correct. You can use two of the second group of points for this treatment, and if you do the second point can be needled with an ear tack or intradermal needle.

When using the divergent channels in this method and the following method certain precautions should be observed.. Since all of the divergent channels pass through the heart, and this treatment is very powerful, you must be very careful with cardiac patients. After any divergent treatment, check to see if CV 17 is painful. If it has a pain reaction, treat the Pericardium Divergent on the painless side of the body, place a magrain pellet on the heart point of the ear, and check to see that CV 17 becomes less sensitive. Here again since all the divergents pass through the heart, it can become strained. Whenever you treat a divergent on one side, treat its opposite polarity paired channel on the other side in the other direction. For instance, if you treat the spleen divergent on the left, treat the stomach divergent on the right.

If the patient is suffering from any acute diseases with floating pulse, do not use the divergents as they may bring the disease deeper into the body.

Magnetic diagnosis of the divergents is also possible. The topographical acupuncturists believe this method reaches the deepest levels of imbalance in the body and it is used for very old, deep, chronic disease. The method also utilizes a diagnostic approach for more superficial energy disturbances. The result is a therapy for both deep divergent root disease and a more superficial imbalance. This is a simplified version of the method taught by Doctor Iriye at a seminar in San Francisco in 1987. This is where we use the cylinder magnet tool referred to in the chapter on magnets.

To begin, find the three traditional pulse positions on the right wrist of your patient. Move towards the elbow one more position and draw a line across the forearm of the patient parallel to the wrist. On that line, draw an x where the line crosses the meridian pathways of the lung, pericardium, and heart. Repeat this process on the left wrist. We now have six x's drawn on the patient, three on each forearm. The radial x on the right arm represents the paired organs of the lung/large intestine, the middle x represents paired organs of the stomach and spleen, and the ulnar x represents the paired organs of the triple warmer and the pericardium. On the left wrist, the radial x represents the paired organs of the heart and small intestine, the middle x represents the liver and gall bladder, and the ulnar x represents the kidneys and urinary bladder. The Yang organs correspond to the distal side of the line. The Yin organs correspond to the proximal side of the line. This line represents a more superficial level of energy than the deep divergent line.

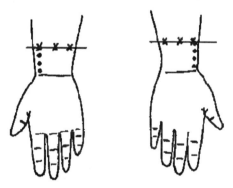

To diagnose the superficial level, simply tape the cylinder magnet to each x one at a time, and do an o-ring test making sure that the north end of the cylinder magnet faces the ulna. Find the two weakest organ pairs. Then tape the cylinder magnet to each of the two weakest organ pairs two times, once with the north facing distally, and once with the north facing proximally and o-ring test each time. If the o-ring test is weakest facing proximally, the Yin organ is most imbalanced, and if the o-ring test is weakest facing distally, the Yang organ is most imbalanced.

Iriye Diagnosis for 12 Major Meridians

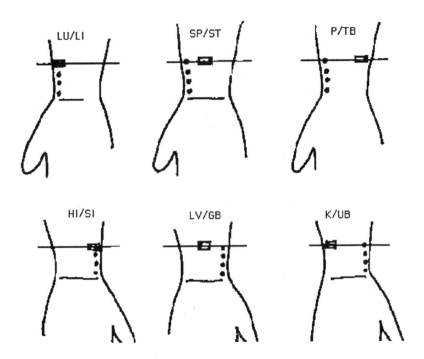

Paired Meridian Diagosis

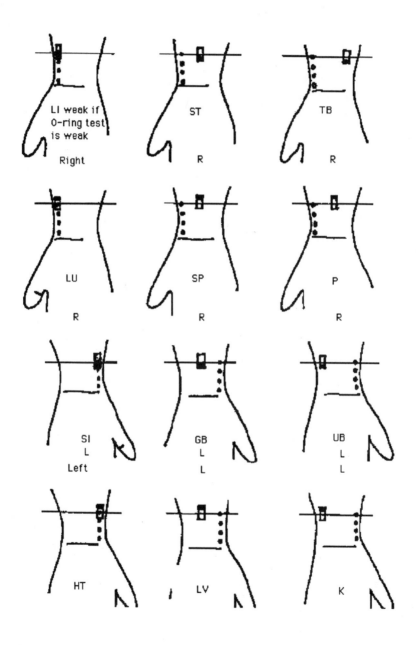

We treat the two most out of balance organs but we must know I which is the primary and which is the secondary. To do this we place one cylinder magnet on one of the weak organ positions with the north facing the weak direction nd another cylinder magnet on the other weak position with the north facing the weak direction. Next we o-ring test again. If the test is strong, the first position is the secondary and the second is primary, and if the test is weak the first position is primary and the second is secondary. In other words, the secondary position will cover the primary position (make the o-ring test strong), but the primary position will not cover the secondary position.

We now treat this imbalance, leaving the first treatment on no more than five minutes, and seven to ten minutes thereafter. The treatment formula is based on Doctor Iriye's personal experience working on this method for over twenty years . The meridians are placed in their six phase paired correspondences for the purposes of this therapy. The results of our testing are then applied to the following chart to get the treatment points. When we get the treatment points we must find which side to treat. This is done by having the patient place their thumb and forefinger on the facial diagnosis points in the illustration and muscle testing each side of the appropriate primary organ imbalance.

The side to treat is the side that shows weakest on the O-ring test. When placing the magnets on the points, be sure to use one north and one south on each side of the body and o-ring test to see which is the correct position. The correct position will show a strong o-ring test.

Type	Location		Abnormal Side		Normal Side Li-Biao	
	Primary	Secondary	Primary	Secondary	Primary	Secondary
Paired	Hand	Foot	Lo	Opposite Lo	Source	Opposite Source
	Foot	Hand	Lo	Source	Source	Lo
Un Paired	Hand	Foot	Lo	Opposite Lo	Source	Opposite Source
	Foot	Hand	Lo	Cleft	Lo	Cleft
	Foot	Foot	Source	Lo	Source	Lo
	Hand	Hand				

The Li-Biao is the Yin/Yang paired Meridian

Paired Organs by the six divisions are:

Urinary Bladder and Small Intestine
Stomach and Large Intestine
Triple Burner and Gall Bladder
Heart and Kidney
Speen and Lung
Pericardium and Liver

Facial Diagnostic Points

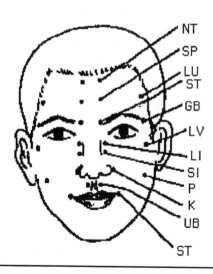

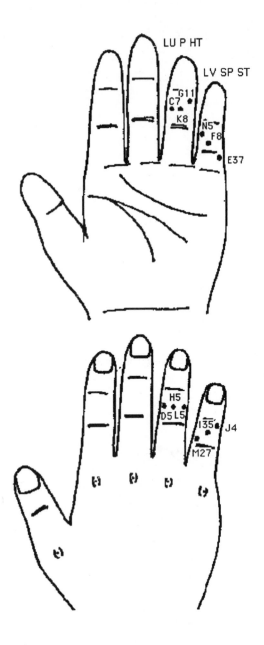

Source Points

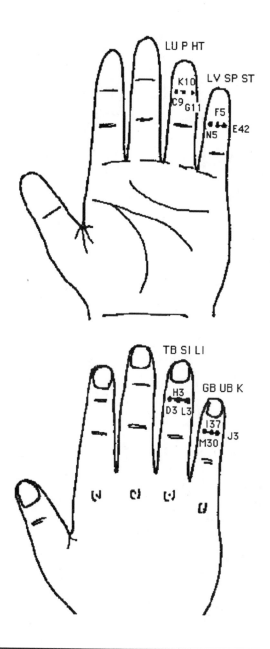

Lo Points

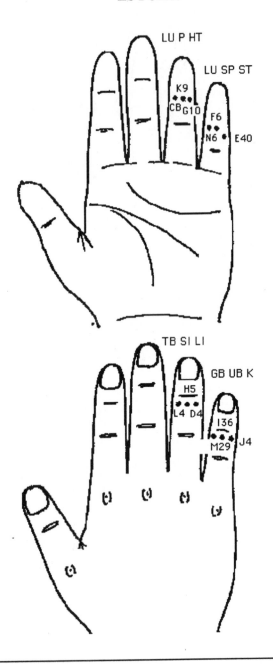

To find which deep divergent meridian to treat, we begin from the line previously drawn four pulse position lengths above the wrist and go proximally upward three more pulse position lengths. Again we mark the six x positions as before. They represent the same organ pairs but the polarity is now reversed—the distal side of the line represents the Yin organs and the proximal side represents the Yang organs. At this deep level of chronic imbalance, it is the Yin organs that are imbalanced ninety percent of the time.

Ireye Diagnostic divergent Meridians

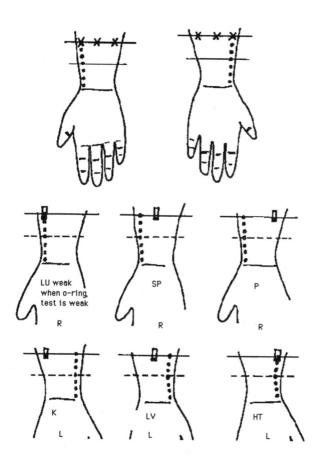

Now, with the north side facing the hand, place the cylinder magnet on each of the six x positions and o-ring test. In this case record all of the positions that are weak. Then decide which position you think is the root imbalance (can be any one) and place a cylinder magnet on that position with north facing the hand. With another cylinder magnet, test all the other positions that were weak. If you have chosen the correct root organ all the previously weak positions will now test strong.

If some positions are strong and some are still weak, or if there is no change in any of them, you must remove both cylinder magnets and choose another root. Test all the other positions again. When you have found the one position that makes all the other positions strong, you have the root divergent imbalance, and that is the one to treat. Treat according to the following chart. The north south polarities shown are the most common, but always check with the o-ring test to be sure. Do the same facial point diagnosis to see which side is the abnormal one and treat the weak o-ring test side. You may use the upper meeting point and both of the other points listed, but use a ear tack or intradermal needle on one of the points (other than the meeting point). The above method is extremely effective in clinic as it gives a root and superficial treatment.

Deep Divergent Meridian Treatment

Li biao Jinglo Tx	-Pole (North)		+Pole (South)		Primary Treatment
Kidney	I37	J4	I8	I13	Yin
Urinary Bladder	I8	I3	I19		Yang
Liver	M30	N5	M1		Yin
Gall Bladder	M1		M30	N5	Yang
Heart	between E2	A29	G11	H3	Yin
Small Intestine	G11	H3	between E2	A29	Yang
Pericardium	M4		K10	L3	Yin
Triple Burner	K10	L3	M4		Yang
Lung	E10		C9	D3	Yin
Large Intestine	C9		E10		Yang
Spleen	E42	F5	E2		Yin
Stomach	E2		E42	F5	Yang

Divergent Meridian Hand Treatments

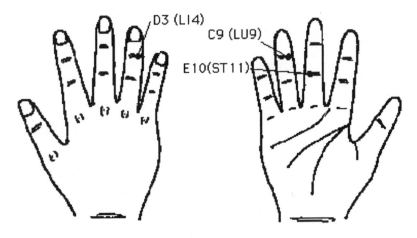

D3 (LI4)
C9 (LU9)
E10(ST11)

Lung/Large Intestine

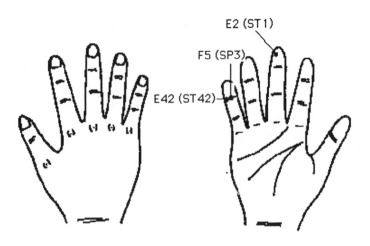

E2 (ST1)
F5 (SP3)
E42 (ST42)

Spleen/Stomach

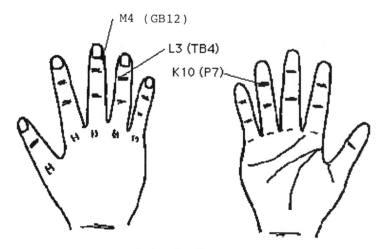

Pericardium/Triple Burner

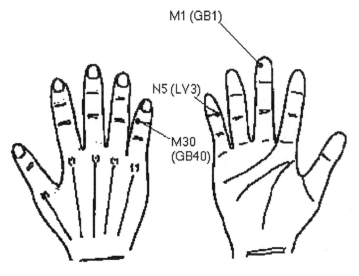

Liver/Gall Bladder

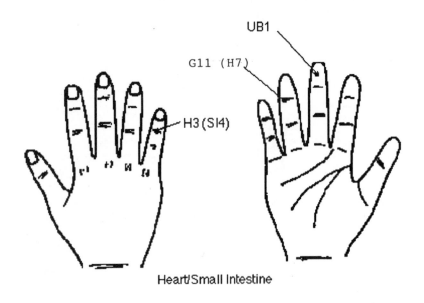

Heart/Small Intestine

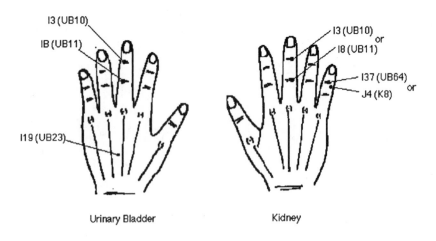

Urinary Bladder

Kidney

Conclusion

I would like to caution all students of energetic medicine to keep an open mind and a constant vigilance. Many gifted masters present seemingly contradictory theories and clinical results, which in a broader view may not be contradictory at all.

Doctor Wae Shui, a traditional Chinese Medical Practioner for over sixty years, gave me a slip of paper with "Practice is the verification of true standard" written on it. In other words—if it works, use it. Doctor Manaka, during his seminar, expressed the belief that we should try various techniques to ascertain their effects.

The basic idea is to seek to broaden our horizons constantly, through study, research, and practice, and to maintain the first principle of alternative medicine—DO NO HARM TO THE PATIENT!

Bibliography

Koryo Hand Acupuncture , Tae Woo Yoo O.M.D., PhD,
  Eum Yang Mek Jin Publishing Co., January 1988.

Introduction to the Chakras, Peter Reader
  Acquarian Press.

Extraordinary Vessels, Kiiko Matsumoto and Steven Birch
  Paradigm Publications, 1986.

The Eight Extra Meridians, Compiled by Kevin R. Jeynes, B.
  Ac., Brisbane College of Traditional Acupuncture and
  Oriental Medicine.

Chakras—Energy Centers of Transformation, Harish JoHari
  Destiny Books, 1987.

Awaken Healing Energy Through the Tao, Mantak Chia,
  Aurora Press, 1983.

Kundalini Yoga for the West, Swami Silananda Radha,
  Shambhala Publications, Inc., 1978.

Taoist Yoga—Alchemy & Immortality, Lu K'uan Yu (Charles
  Luk),
  Samuel Weiser, Inc., 1984.

The Secondary Vessels of Acupucture, Royston Low,
  Borsons Publishers Limited, 1983.

Lecture Notes, Kiiko Matsumoto.

Lecture Notes, Leuk De Schepper.

Lecture Notes, Japanese American Acupuncture Foundation.

Lecture Notes, Dr. Yoshi Manaka.

North American College of Acupuncture, Correspondence
Course Material
     Kok Yuew Liong
     P.O. Box 12128
     Salem, Oregon 97309 (1980)

Acupucture: A Comprehensive Text , Translated and Edited by
John O' Connor and Dan Bensky
     Eastland Press, 1981.

Color and Crystals: A Journey Through the Chakras, Joy
Gardner.
     The Crossing Press, 1988.

Essentials of Chinese Acupuncture, compiled by Beijing College
of Traditional Chinese Medicine, Shanghai College of Chinese
Medicine, Nanjing College of Chinese Medicine.

The Acupuncture Institute of the Academy of Chinese Medicine
     Foreign Language Press, Beijing, 1980.

ORDER FORM

WHITE ELEPHANT MONASTERY
P. O. BOX 523
SAN FRANCISCO, CA 94101

"Magnetic Healing and Meditation" at $12.95 each _____

California residents add $6^{1}/2$ % sales tax _____

Shipping and handling:

Book Rate   First book $1.00 _____

Each additional book .50 _____

Air Mail $2.50 each book _____

TOTAL _____

Enclosed find my check or money order for _____ to cover the

cost of _____ copies of "Magnetic Healing and Meditation" plus tax

(if CA resident) and shipping.

Please send books to:

Name _____

Address _____

City/State _____ Zip _____

Outside U.S. - Air Mail Only
Foreign orders must be prepaid at
current exchange rates in U.S. dollars.

CONTACT WHITE ELEPHANT MONASTERY
FOR SEMINARS AND GROUP CONSULTATIONS!